W9-CXP-715

A SECOND
STORYTELLER'S CHOICE

A Second Storyteller's Choice

A selection of stories,
with notes on how to tell them by
EILEEN COLWELL

With drawings by
PRUDENCE SEWARD

HENRY Z. WALCK Inc.
NEW YORK

With love to

ELEANOR FARJEON

who could tell stories

'as never so'

Library of Congress Catalog Card Number : 65–17630

All rights reserved
This collection © The Bodley Head Ltd 1965
Illustrations © The Bodley Head Ltd 1965
Printed in Great Britain
First American edition 1965
Second American edition 1966
Third American edition 1967

ACKNOWLEDGMENTS

Every effort has been made to trace the ownership of the copyright material in this book. It is the publishers' belief that the necessary permissions from publishers, authors and authorized agents have been obtained, but in the event of any question arising as to the use of any material, the publishers, while expressing regret for any error unconsciously made, will be pleased to make the necessary correction in future editions of this book.

Thanks are due to the following for permission to reprint copyright material: Edmund Ward Ltd for 'The Knockers' from *The Mermaid of Zennor* by Eileen Molony; Dr Arthur Ransome for 'Salt' from *Old Peter's Russian Tales*, published by Thomas Nelson & Sons Ltd, London and New York; George G. Harrap & Co Ltd and Houghton Mifflin Company, Boston, for 'The Story of Epaminondas and his Auntie' from *Stories to Tell to Children* by Sara Cone Bryant; the University of London Press Ltd for 'The Story of Brother Johannick and his Silver Bell' from *Tales for Jack and Jane* by Elizabeth Clark; Miss E. M. Almedingen and J. B. Lippincott Co., New York, for 'Volkh's Journey to the East' from *The Knights of the Golden Table*, published by The Bodley Head Ltd; Thomas Y. Crowell Company, New York, Publishers, for 'Did you Feed my Cow?', 'Mr Rabbit', and 'Old Ponto' from *Did you Feed my Cow?* by Margaret Taylor, Copyright © 1956 by Margaret Taylor; Miss Eleanor Farjeon for 'Bertha Goldfoot' from *The Old Nurse's Stocking Basket*, published by the University of London Press; the Oxford University Press, Toronto, and Henry Z. Walck, Inc., New York, for 'The Golden Phoenix' from *The Golden Phoenix and Other French Canadian Tales* by Marius Barbeau and Michael Hornyansky; the Executors of the late Frank Worthington for 'The Hare, the Lions, the Monkey and Hare's Spotted Blanket' from *African Aesop*, published by William Collins; The Literary Trustees of Walter de la Mare and the Society of Authors as their representative for 'The Dancing Princesses' from *Tales Told Again*, published by Faber & Faber and Alfred A. Knopf; Holt, Rinehart & Winston, Inc, Publishers, New York, for 'The Goat Well' from *The Fire on the Mountain* by Harold Courlander and Wolf Leslau, Copyright 1950 by Holt, Rinehart & Winston, Inc; Nattali & Maurice Ltd for 'The Snooks Family' from *Tales from Ebony* by Harcourt Williams; Harper & Row, publishers, for 'Jean Labadie's Big Black Dog' from *The Talking Cat and other Stories of French Canada* by Natalie Savage Carlson, Copyright 1952 by Natalie Savage Carlson; Mrs Ruth Manning-Sanders for 'Zini and the Witches' from *Red Indian Folk and Fairy Tales*, published by the Oxford University

Press, London, and Roy Publishers; the Oxford University Press, London, and Henry Z. Walck, Inc., New York, for 'Where Arthur Sleeps' from *Welsh Legends and Folk Tales* by Gwyn Jones.

CONTENTS

Preface

MY FIRST *Storyteller's Choice* was a very personal selection of stories I particularly loved and had shared successfully with children. This, my second collection, is also of stories we have enjoyed together many times, but it consists mainly of traditional tales which are reasonably easy to tell and which appeal to a rather younger age group.

When they listen to stories, children expect action, characters in whom they can believe and pleasure in a tale well told. I have had this in mind in making this selection from the many stories I know. All the stories in this book are favourites with children and are here in the versions most effective for telling—hence the French-Canadian variant of *The Golden Phoenix* and the Welsh retelling of the King Arthur legend. Familiar tales like *Epaminondas* will be found, but also lesser known material such as the Russian *Volkh's Journey to the East* and *The Goat Well* from Ethiopia. De la Mare's re-creation of Grimm's *The Dancing Shoes* is here because it is such a wonderful example of what happens to a story in the hands of a poet. *Bertha Goldfoot* by Eleanor Farjeon shows how a modern writer can catch the authentic ring and feeling of a folk-tale. Nearly all the stories in this book have humour, for children love to laugh.

If we remember, if we can still feel what it was like as a child to fall under the spell of a well told story, we know that children *need* stories for their happiness and development.

'Give them stories . . . Give them wings!'

EILEEN COLWELL

A SECOND
STORYTELLER'S CHOICE

The Knockers

AT THE bottom of every mine in the world you'll find a Cornishman, but only at the bottom of a Cornish tin mine will you find a Knocker. For of all the fairies in Cornwall the Knockers are seldomest seen.

There aren't as many now, as there were, but a hundred years ago they were as common as moles. The length and breadth of Cornwall was riddled with their little tunnels and underground workings.

You can still see these all along the coast; little narrow caves opening out on to the cliff face, with the sea rushing up them at high tide making a roaring blowing sound, and the water piling up inside the mine shafts, until the cliff becomes a mere shell to a boiling cauldron of sea-water.

It isn't easy to tell now, which of these passages were tunnelled by the Knockers, and which by the miners themselves, but there are some no more than twelve inches high. No mortal man could have bored them so far into the cliff, and no man was ever small enough to pass along them.

If you ask a miner about them to-day, he will tell you they are 'the old men's workings', by which he means the Knockers.

Billy Chenoweth and his father worked at a tin mine called Wheal Prudence, no more than a couple of miles from Perranzabuloe, where the blessed St Piran himself wandered among the sand dunes, and saw the rich veins of red and green metal buried deep in the hard rock, and where he first taught the Cornish miners how to get their tin.

Wheal Prudence stood high up on the headland. A great ragged slate-grey tower marked the spot where the shaft was sunk, and a tiny red stream tumbled, like a rusty waterfall, over beds of fine black sand, down to the beach below.

Billy was only nine, but he was a sturdy little boy, with a fierce crop of stiff black hair, and blue eyes, and he worked so hard that his father, Elisha Chenoweth, said he was as useful as a fully-grown tinner.

But Billy's legs were short, and he couldn't quite manage to climb all the way down the steep iron ladder to the place where his father worked.

So Elisha Chenoweth would carry him down the dark shaft on his back. Once there, it was Billy's job to push the barrows of ore along the rolley-way to the shaft, so they could be hauled up to the top.

If Elisha managed to hew out a lot of tin with his pick, then he and Billy were rich. But if the place they were given to work was a poor one, then they had to struggle like beavers to find enough money to live on.

Although Billy had never actually seen a Knocker, he knew there were plenty of them about at Wheal Prudence, for an old man called Chinery Williams had told him about them.

Once Billy had found a tiny pick, made from a stag's horn, too small to be of use to man or boy. There was one part of the mine where you could hear the Knockers hammering away in nearby passages. Neither Chinery, nor any of the other miners would consent to work there, for there was no knowing what the little men would do if they were vexed.

But there was one particular Knocker who was the miners' friend. His name was Blue-cap, and the older miners would tell how he would settle on the barrows in the shape of a little blue flame, and then, suddenly of their own accord, they would start bowling along down to the rolley-way, as if unseen arms were pushing them.

'But if ever Blue-cap should do you a service, boy Billy,' Chinery would say, 'be sure to leave him his wages. He can be main useful to you if you treat him friendly.' And Billy would nod his head sagely and promise that he would.

In fact, if Elisha had known as much about the Knockers

as Billy did, he would not have made such a stupid mistake. But it all turned out for the best in the end.

It was Billy's birthday, and his mother had made a hand-some blackberry pasty for their lunch. It was shaped like a half-moon, with crinkly patterns of good hot flaky pastry, where the purple blackberry juice trickled up through the edges, and, before she sealed the end, Billy's mother had taken care to pack in a spoonful of thick, golden-crusted Cornish cream.

So it wasn't surprising, you see, that when the Knockers smelt it they got hungry, nor was it surprising either that Elisha was greedy.

It was all a little unfortunate.

When dinner time came round and Elisha and Billy sat down to eat their pasties, Billy could hardly *wait* to sink his strong white teeth into the blackberries, and when he did—well—the pasty was gone before you could say 'One-o'clock.'

Now Elisha's teeth weren't so good as Billy's, so he ate his pasty slower, and he hadn't had more than a couple of bites when he stopped suddenly. Close behind them, as plain as they could be, they heard a tiny voice saying:

> 'Chenoweth, Chenoweth!
> Thy pasty be tasty,
> So leave some for Knocker
> And don't eat so hasty.'

'Blow me! If it isn't they Knockers!' said Billy. 'Can you hear them, father? Don't eat all your pasty, but leave some for the Knockers.'

But either Elisha couldn't, or wouldn't, hear them, for he sunk his teeth deep into the blackberry pasty, and he didn't stop until he had finished every crumb.

Billy began to feel frightened, and then a little voice came again from just beside them:

'Chenoweth, Chenoweth!
Thou proper old nasty,
Bad luck from the Knocker
For wolfing thy pasty.'

Billy saw that things were going to get serious, as indeed they did, but he was a sensible little boy and he didn't say anything to Elisha.

Poor Elisha! It did not take more than one blow of his pick to do it. As he struck the rock, a shower of stones and small boulders became dislodged. He was sent spinning to the ground, and almost buried beneath the heap of rubble.

Billy ran to a nearby passage for Chinery Williams and three of the other miners, and they dug Elisha out with spades and carried him up to the top of the shaft and sent him back to his wife with a very badly crushed arm.

Elisha was ill a long time, and no money came into the house. Billy's mother would not let him go down the mine alone, although she was at her wits' end to know how to get enough soups and jellies and other good food for Elisha.

'Blow me!' said Billy one day, 'I *must* earn some more money somehow. Even if I don't tell mother about it, I must get back to the mine.'

Now seventy fathoms of iron ladder are one thing when you go down them pick-a-back, but they're quite a different matter if you go down them on your own short legs.

Billy counted the rungs of each ladder as he went down hand over hand.

By the time he had gone down twenty fathoms his legs felt as if they were stuffed with red-hot needles. By the time he had gone down forty fathoms he felt as if he had climbed a mountain. By the time he had gone down fifty fathoms, he did not believe he had any legs, for they had stopped hurting. And by the time he had gone down sixty fathoms he had lost count and forgotten his way.

He groped and stumbled along a new, strange passage,

pushing a stone in front of him as his father had taught him to do, in case he should come across a pit suddenly in the darkness.

The next thing he remembered was hearing the stone splash as it bounded down a disused shaft and hit the water seventy feet below.

'Blow me!' said Billy, as he thought of the yawning drop below him, and lay flat on his face in the disused passage, because he felt giddy.

After a while he began to wonder whether he ought not to try and grope his way back again to the main shaft. Then, to his great relief, he caught the sound of footsteps.

He listened carefully, and thought that quite a lot of people must be climbing up the disused shaft, but the foot-steps were small and light, as a child's might be.

He felt a little scared, and tried to shout out loud 'Who's there?' but no sound came.

The footsteps drew nearer, and suddenly, over the top of the shaft came a procession of small blue lights, each one about two feet from the ground.

Billy shrank back into the side of the rock passage and lay low.

He knew who was in the procession—the Knockers! But he was afraid to speak or to let them know he was there.

He lay still, and the stream of little men passed quite close by him.

They were dressed like his father, or Chinery, or any of the other tinners. Each wore a little coarse drill jacket and trousers. On the brim of each hard battered bowler hat glowed a little candle with a tiny blue flame. Each had a bunch of spare candles knotted to his top buttonhole, and over their shoulders they carried little stags' horn picks, like the one Billy had found.

Billy saw at once what had happened. He must have strayed on to Knocker's Ground.

The little band passed by, and when they had gone Billy

realised for the first time how forlorn he was. He wished he had spoken to them.

'Blow me!' he said, 'they might have been able to help me. I must run after them.'

He struggled to his feet, but his knee joints were still stiff and weak from the long climb down the shaft, and he could barely stand.

Just as he was giving up all hope, he heard a tiny breathless voice behind him saying, 'I'm late, I'm late, I'm some late, my patience!' and turning round he saw one of the Knockers had got left behind.

This time Billy didn't hesitate. 'If you please, sir,' he said, 'I've lost my way. Can you help me at all?'

'My dear soul!' said the Knocker backing away from him, 'if it isn't one of they mischieevious boys. Did you ever hear tell of such a thing! How did you come to be on Knocker's Ground?'

'My father's sick,' said Billy, 'and I come down to make some money. I lost my way.' And he told the Knocker the whole story.

'Did you ever hear tell of Blue-cap?' said the Knocker, when he had finished.

'That I did,' said Billy, 'he's the Knocker they do call the miners' friend. Chinery Williams has told me about him.'

The Knocker's small wide mouth crinkled up into a grin. 'Ah,' he said, 'Chinery do know me. You're as near to Blue-cap now as you're ever likely to be.'

Then he told Billy that when he got back again to the main shaft he was to be sure and remember the way to the Knocker's passage.

'And next time you look for tin,' he said, 'look here. Meantime, if you want to get up they old ladders, ask Chinery to carry you. You'll need all the breath in your body to load the barrows to-morrow. You see if you don't.'

'That's main kind of you,' said Billy, 'but how am I to get back to the shaft? I can hardly walk.'

'You're too big for me to carry,' said the Knocker, 'but you settle down and sleep a while. I'll see the miners aren't too long finding you. If they hear my pick at work they'll follow me.'

So Billy did as he was told, and lay down quietly and went to sleep. There Chinery found him a few hours later.

'Your mother, poor soul, has been out of her mind looking for you,' scolded Chinery. But he picked Billy up in his arms very gently and carried him up the shaft.

Billy had a brave job of it, though, to get him to take him down the pit again next day. 'Your mother will have the skin off my back for doing it,' Chinery said, 'but I suppose if you've a mind to it you'll get down somehow, even if I don't take you.'

So every day after that Billy was carried down the pit by one of the miners.

However the boy managed to pick all the tin he did was a mystery to them.

At the end of every day his barrow would come trundling along with as much tin inside as a grown man could have shifted.

The younger miners were fair mazed by it, but Chinery would shake his head and say the boy carried 'Knockers' Luck' along with him.

Elisha Chenoweth got better quickly on all the jellies and good food Billy was able to buy for him. But there was one point on which Billy was firm.

Before he handed his wages over to his mother, he always kept back a certain sum which he hid in a secret place in the mine.

'Blow me!' he would say, 'but that Blue-cap earns his wages!'

And every Friday morning he would ask his mother to be sure and bake an extra blackberry pasty for the little Knockers.

From *The Mermaid of Zennor* by Eileen Molony (Edmund Ward, London)

(See Note, page 149)

Salt

ONCE UPON a time there were three brothers, and their father was a great merchant who sent his ships far over the sea, and traded here and there in many countries. Well, the names of the two elder brothers do not matter, but the youngest was called Ivan the Ninny, because he was always playing and never working; and if there was a silly thing to do, why, off he went and did it. And so, when the brothers grew up, the father sent the two elder ones off, each in a fine ship laden with gold and jewels, and rings and bracelets, and laces and silks, and sticks with little bits of silver hammered into their handles, and spoons with patterns of blue and red, and everything else you can think of that costs too much to buy. But he made Ivan the Ninny stay at home, and did not give him a ship at all. Ivan saw his brothers go sailing off over the sea on a summer morning, to make their fortunes and come back rich men; and then, for the first time in his life, he wanted to work and do something useful. He went to his father and kissed his hand, and he kissed the hand of his little old mother, and he begged his father to give him a ship so that he could try his fortune like his brothers.

'But you have never done a wise thing in your life, and no one could count all the silly things you've done if he spent a hundred days in counting,' said his father.

'True,' said Ivan; 'but now I am going to be wise, and sail the sea and come back with something in my pockets to show that I am not a ninny any longer. Give me just a little ship, father mine—just a little ship for myself.'

'Give him a little ship,' said the mother. 'He may not be a ninny after all.'

'Very well,' said his father. 'I will give him a little ship;

but I am not going to waste good roubles by giving him a rich cargo.'

'Give me any cargo you like,' said Ivan.

So his father gave him a little ship, a little old ship, and a cargo of rags and scraps and things that were not fit for anything but to be thrown away. And he gave him a crew of ancient old sailormen who were past work; and Ivan went on board and sailed away at sunset, like the ninny he was. And the feeble, ancient, old sailormen pulled up the ragged, dirty sails, and away they went over the sea to learn what fortune, good or bad, God had in mind for a crew of old men with a ninny for a master.

The fourth day after they set sail there came a great wind over the sea. The feeble old men did the best they could with the ship; but the old, torn sails tore from the masts, and the wind did what it pleased, and threw the little ship on an unknown island away in the middle of the sea. Then the wind dropped, and left the little ship on the beach, and Ivan the Ninny and his ancient old men, like good Russians, praising God that they were still alive.

'Well, children,' said Ivan, for he knew how to talk to sailors, 'do you stay here and mend the sails, and make new ones out of the rags we carry as cargo, while I go inland and see if there is anything that could be of use to us.'

So the ancient old sailormen sat on deck with their legs crossed, and made sails out of rags, of torn scraps of old brocades, of soiled embroidered shawls, of all the rubbish that they had with them for a cargo. You never saw such sails. The tide came up and floated the ship, and they threw out anchors at bow and stern, and sat there in the sunlight, making sails and patching them and talking of the days when they were young. All this while Ivan the Ninny went walking off into the island.

Now in the middle of that island was a high mountain, a high mountain it was, and so white that when he came near it Ivan the Ninny began thinking of sheepskin coats, although it was midsummer and the sun was hot in the sky. The trees were green round about, but there was nothing growing on the mountain at all. It was just a great white mountain piled up into the sky in the middle of a green island. Ivan walked a little way up the white slopes of the mountain, and then,

because he felt thirsty, he thought he would let a little snow melt in his mouth. He took some in his fingers and stuffed it in. Quickly enough it came out again, I can tell you, for the mountain was not made of snow but of good Russian salt.

Ivan the Ninny did not stop to think twice. The salt was so clean and shone so brightly in the sunlight. He just turned round and ran back to the shore, and called out to his ancient old sailormen and told them to empty everything they had on board over into the sea. Over it all went, rags and tags and rotten timbers, till the little ship was as empty as a soup bowl after supper. And then those ancient old men were set to work carrying salt from the mountain and taking it on board the little ship, and stowing it away below deck till there was not room for another grain. Ivan the Ninny would have liked to take the whole mountain, but there was not room in the little ship. And for that the ancient old sailormen thanked God, be-cause their backs ached and their old legs were weak, and they said they would have died if they had had to carry any more.

Then they hoisted up the new sails they had patched together out of the rags and scraps of shawls and old brocades, and they sailed away once more over the blue sea. And the wind stood fair, and they sailed before it, and the ancient old sailors rested their backs, and told old tales, and took turn and turn about at the rudder.

And after many days' sailing they came to a town, with towers and churches and painted roofs, all set on the side of a hill that sloped down into the sea. At the foot of the hill was a quiet harbour, and they sailed in there and moored the ship and hauled down their patch-work sails.

Ivan the Ninny went ashore, and took with him a little bag of clean white salt to show what kind of goods he had for sale, and he asked his way to the palace of the Tzar of that town. He came to the palace, and went in and bowed to the ground before the Tzar.

'Who are you?' says the Tzar.

'I, great lord, am a Russian merchant, and here in a bag is

some of my merchandise, and I beg your leave to trade with your subjects in this town.'

'Let me see what is in the bag,' says the Tzar.

Ivan the Ninny took a handful from the bag and showed it to the Tzar.

'What is it?' says the Tzar.

'Good Russian salt,' says Ivan the Ninny.

Now in that country they had never heard of salt, and the Tzar looked at the salt, and he looked at Ivan and he laughed.

'Why, this,' says he, 'is nothing but white dust, and that we can pick up for nothing. The men of my town have no need to trade with you. You must be a ninny.'

Ivan grew red, for he knew what his father used to call him. He was ashamed to say anything. So he bowed to the ground, and went away out of the palace.

But when he was outside he thought to himself, 'I wonder what sort of salt they use in these parts if they do not know good Russian salt when they see it. I will go to the kitchen.'

So he went round to the back door of the palace, and put his head into the kitchen, and said, 'I am very tired. May I sit down here and rest a little while?'

'Come in,' says one of the cooks. 'But you must sit just there, and not put even your little finger in the way of us; for we are the Tzar's cooks, and we are in the middle of making ready his dinner.' And the cook put a stool in a corner out of the way, and Ivan slipped in round the door, and sat down in the corner and looked about him. There were seven cooks at least, boiling and baking, and stewing and toasting, and roasting and frying. And as for scullions, they were as thick as cockroaches, dozens of them, running to and fro, tumbling over each other, and helping the cooks.

Ivan the Ninny sat on his stool, with his legs tucked under him and the bag of salt on his knees. He watched the cooks and the scullions, but he did not see them put anything in the dishes which he thought could take the place of salt. No; the meat was without salt, the kasha was without salt, and there was no salt in the potatoes. Ivan nearly turned sick at the thought of the tastelessness of all that food.

There came the moment when all the cooks and scullions ran out of the kitchen to fetch the silver platters on which to lay the dishes. Ivan slipped down from his stool, and running from stove to stove, from saucepan to frying pan, he dropped a pinch of salt, just what was wanted, no more no less, in every one of the dishes. Then he ran back to the stool in the corner, and sat there, and watched the dishes being put on the silver platters and carried off in gold-embroidered napkins to be the dinner of the Tzar.

The Tzar sat at table and took his first spoonful of soup.

'The soup is very good to-day,' says he, and he finishes the soup to the last drop.

'I've never known the soup so good,' says the Tzaritza, and she finishes hers.

'This is the best soup I ever tasted,' says the Princess, and down goes hers, and she, you know, was the prettiest princess who ever had dinner in this world.

It was the same with the kasha and the same with the meat. The Tzar and the Tzaritza and the Princess wondered why they had never had so good a dinner in all their lives before.

'Call the cooks,' says the Tzar. And they called the cooks, and all the cooks came in, and bowed to the ground, and stood in a row before the Tzar.

'What did you put in the dishes to-day that you never put before?' says the Tzar.

'We put nothing unusual, your greatness,' say the cooks, and bowed to the ground again.

'Then why do the dishes taste better?'

'We do not know, your greatness,' say the cooks.

'Call the scullions,' says the Tzar. And the scullions were called, and they too bowed to the ground, and stood in a row before the Tzar.

'What was done in the kitchen to-day that has not been done there before?' says the Tzar.

'Nothing, your greatness,' say all the scullions except one.

And that one scullion bowed again, and kept on bowing, and then he said, 'Please, your greatness, please, great lord, there is usually none in the kitchen but ourselves; but to-day there was a young Russian merchant, who sat on a stool in the corner and said he was tired.'

'Call the merchant,' says the Tzar.

So they brought in Ivan the Ninny, and he bowed before the Tzar, and stood there with his little bag of salt in his hand.

'Did you do anything to my dinner?' says the Tzar.

'I did, your greatness,' says Ivan.

'What did you do?'

'I put a pinch of Russian salt in every dish.'

'That white dust?' says the Tzar.

'Nothing but that.'

'Have you got any more of it?'

'I have a little ship in the harbour laden with nothing else,' says Ivan.

'It is the most wonderful dust in the world,' says the Tzar, 'and I will buy every grain of it you have. What do you want for it?'

Ivan the Ninny scratched his head and thought. He thought that if the Tzar liked it as much as all that it must be worth a fair price, so he said, 'We will put the salt into bags, and for every bag of salt you must give me three bags of the same weight—one of gold, one of silver, and one of precious stones. Cheaper than that, your greatness, I could not possibly sell.'

'Agreed,' says the Tzar. 'And a cheap price, too, for a dust so full of magic that it makes dull dishes tasty, and tasty dishes so good that there is no looking away from them.'

So all the day long, and far into the night, the ancient old sailormen bent their backs under sacks of salt, and bent them again under sacks of gold and silver and precious stones. When all the salt had been put in the Tzar's treasury—yes, with twenty soldiers guarding it with great swords shining in the moonlight—and when the little ship was loaded with riches, so that even the deck was piled high with precious stones, the ancient old men lay down among the jewels and slept till morning, when Ivan the Ninny went to bid good-bye to the Tzar.

'And whither shall you sail now?' asked the Tzar.

' I shall sail away to Russia in my little ship,' says Ivan.

And the Princess, who was very beautiful, said, 'A little Russian ship?'

'Yes,' says Ivan.

'I have never seen a Russian ship,' says the Princess, and she begs her father to let her go to the harbour with her nurses and maids, to see the little Russian ship before Ivan set sail.

She came with Ivan to the harbour, and the ancient old sailormen took them on board.

She ran all over the ship, looking now at this and now at that, and Ivan told her the names of everything—deck, mast, and rudder.

'May I see the sails?' she asked. And the ancient old men hoisted the ragged sails, and the wind filled the sails and tugged.

'Why doesn't the ship move when the sails are up?' asked the Princess.

'The anchor holds her,' said Ivan.

'Please let me see the anchor,' says the Princess.

'Haul up the anchor, my children, and show it to the Princess,' says Ivan to the ancient old sailormen.

And the old men hauled up the anchor, and showed it to the Princess; and she said it was a very good little anchor. But, of course, as soon as the anchor was up the ship began to move. One of the ancient old men bent over the tiller, and, with a fair wind behind her, the little ship slipped out of the harbour and away to the blue sea. When the Princess looked round, thinking it was time to go home, the little ship was far

from land, and away in the distance she could only see the
gold towers of her father's palace, glittering like pin points
in the sunlight. Her nurses and maids wrung their hands and
made an outcry, and the Princess sat down on a heap of
jewels, and put a handkerchief to her eyes, and cried and
cried and cried.

Ivan the Ninny took her hands and comforted her, and told
her of the wonders of the sea that he would show her, and
the wonders of the land. And she looked up at him while he
talked, and his eyes were kind and hers were sweet; and the
end of it was that they were both very well content, and
agreed to have a marriage feast as soon as the little ship
should bring them to the home of Ivan's father. Merry was
that voyage. All day long Ivan and the Princess sat on deck
and said sweet things to each other, and at twilight they sang
songs, and drank tea, and told stories. As for the nurses and
maids, the Princess told them to be glad; and so they danced
and clapped their hands, and ran about the ship, and teased
the ancient old sailormen.

When they had been sailing many days, the Princess was
looking out over the sea, and she cried out to Ivan, 'See, over
there, far away, are two big ships with white sails, not like
our sails of brocade and bits of silk.'

Ivan looked, shading his eyes with his hands.

'Why, those are the ships of my elder brothers,' said he.
'We shall all sail home together.'

And he made the ancient old sailormen give a hail in their
cracked old voices. And the brothers heard them, and came on
board to greet Ivan and his bride. And when they saw that
she was a Tzar's daughter, and that the very decks were
heaped with precious stones, because there was no room
below, they said one thing to Ivan and something else to each
other.

To Ivan they said, 'Thanks be to God, He has given you
good trading.'

But to each other, 'How can this be?' says one. 'Ivan the

Ninny bringing back such a cargo, while we in our fine ships have only a bag or two of gold?'

'And what is Ivan the Ninny doing with a princess?' says the other.

And they ground their teeth, and waited their time, and came up suddenly, when Ivan was alone in the twilight, and picked him up by his head and his heels, and hove him overboard into the dark blue sea.

Not one of the old men had seen them, and the Princess was not on deck. In the morning they said that Ivan the Ninny must have walked overboard in his sleep. And they drew lots. The eldest brother took the Princess, and the second brother took the little ship laden with gold and silver and precious stones. And so the brothers sailed home very well content. But the Princess sat and wept all day long, looking down into the blue water. The elder brother could not comfort her, and the second brother did not try. And the ancient old sailormen muttered in their beards, and were sorry, and prayed to God to give rest to Ivan's soul; for although he had been a ninny, and although he had made them carry a lot of salt and other things, yet they loved him, because he knew how to talk to ancient old sailormen.

But Ivan was not dead. As soon as he splashed into the water, he crammed his fur hat a little tighter on his head, and began swimming in the sea. He swam about until the sun rose, and then, not far away, he saw a floating timber log, and he swam to the log, and got astride of it, and thanked God. And he sat there on the log in the middle of the sea, twiddling his thumbs for want of something to do.

There was a strong current in the sea that carried him along, and at last, after floating for many days without ever a bite for his teeth or a drop for his gullet, his feet touched land. Now that was at night, and he left the log and walked up out of the sea, and lay down on the shore and waited for morning.

When the sun rose he stood up, and saw that he was on a

bare island, and he saw nothing at all on the island except a huge house as big as a mountain; and as he was looking at the house the great door creaked with a noise like that of a hurricane among the pine forests, and opened; and a giant came walking out, and came to the shore, and stood there, looking down at Ivan.

'What are you doing here, little one?' says the giant.

Ivan told him the whole story, just as I have told it to you.

The giant listened to the very end, pulling at his monstrous whiskers. Then he said, 'Listen, little one. I know more of the story than you, for I can tell you that to-morrow morning your eldest brother is going to marry your Princess. But there is no need for you to take on about it. If you want to be there, I will carry you and set you down before the house in time for the wedding. And a fine wedding it is like to be, for your father thinks well of those brothers of yours bringing back all those precious stones, and silver and gold enough to buy a kingdom.'

And with that he picked up Ivan the Ninny and set him on his great shoulders, and set off striding through the sea.

He went so fast that the wind of his going blew off Ivan's hat.

'Stop a moment,' shouts Ivan; 'my hat has blown off.'

'We can't turn back for that,' says the giant; 'we have already left your hat five hundred versts behind us.' And he rushed on, splashing through the sea. The sea was up to his armpits. He rushed on, and the sea was up to his waist. He rushed on, and before the sun had climbed to the top of the blue sky he was splashing up out of the sea with the water about his ankles. He lifted Ivan from his shoulders and set him on the ground.

'Now,' says he, 'little man, off you run, and you'll be in time for the feast. But don't you dare to boast about riding on my shoulders. If you open your mouth about that you'll smart for it, if I have to come ten thousand thousand versts.'

Ivan the Ninny thanked the giant for carrying him through the sea, promised that he would not boast, and then ran off to his father's house. Long before he got there he heard the musicians in the courtyard playing as if they wanted to wear out their instruments before night. The wedding feast had begun, and when Ivan ran in, there, at the high board, was sitting the Princess, and beside her his eldest brother. And there were his father and mother, his second brother, and all the guests. And every one of them was as merry as could be, except the Princess, and she was as white as the salt he had sold to her father.

Suddenly the blood flushed into her cheeks. She saw Ivan in the doorway. Up she jumped at the high board, and cried out, 'There, there is my true love, and not this man who sits beside me at the table.'

'What is this?' says Ivan's father, and in a few minutes knew the whole story.

He turned the two elder brothers out of doors, gave their ships to Ivan, married him to the Princess, and made him his heir. And the wedding feast began again, and they sent for the ancient old sailormen to take part in it. And the ancient old sailormen wept with joy when they saw Ivan and the Princess, like two sweet pigeons, sitting side by side; yes, and they lifted their flagons with their old shaking hands, and cheered with their old cracked voices, and poured the wine down their dry old throats.

There was wine enough and to spare, beer too, and mead—enough to drown a herd of cattle. And as the guests drank and grew merry and proud they set to boasting. This one bragged of his riches, that one of his wife. Another boasted of his cunning, another of his new house, another of his strength, and this one was angry because they would not let him show he could lift the table on one hand. They all drank Ivan's health, and he drank theirs, and in the end he could not bear to listen to their proud boasts.

'That's all very well,' says he, 'but I am the only man in

the world who rode on the shoulders of a giant to come to his wedding feast.'

The words were scarcely out of his mouth before there were a tremendous trampling and a roar of a great wind. The house shook with the footsteps of the giant as he strode up. The giant bent down over the courtyard and looked in at the feast.

'Little man, little man,' says he, 'you promised not to boast of me. I told you what would come if you did, and here you are and have boasted already.'

'Forgive me,' says Ivan, 'it was the drink that boasted, not I.'

'What sort of drink is it that knows how to boast?' says the giant.

'You shall taste it,' says Ivan.

And he made his ancient old sailormen roll a great barrel of wine into the yard, more than enough for a hundred men, and after that a barrel of beer that was as big, and then a barrel of mead that was no smaller.

'Try the taste of that,' says Ivan the Ninny.

Well, the giant did not wait to be asked twice. He lifted the barrel of wine as if it had been a little glass, and emptied it down his throat. He lifted the barrel of beer as if it had been an acorn, and emptied it after the wine. Then he lifted the barrel of mead as if it had been a very small pea, and swallowed every drop of mead that was in it. And after that he began stamping about and breaking things. Houses fell to pieces this way and that, and trees were swept flat like grass. Every step the giant took was followed by the crash of breaking timbers. Then suddenly he fell flat on his back and slept. For three days and nights he slept without waking. At last he opened his eyes.

'Just look about you,' says Ivan, 'and see the damage you've done.'

'And did that little drop of drink make me do all that?' says the giant. 'Well, well, I can well understand that a

2+

drink like that can do a bit of bragging. And after that,' says he, looking at the wrecks of houses, and all the broken things scattered about—'after that,' says he, 'you can boast of me for a thousand years, and I'll have nothing to say against you.'

And he tugged at his great whiskers, and wrinkled his eyes, and went striding off into the sea.

That is the story about salt, and how it made a rich man of Ivan the Ninny, and besides, gave him the prettiest wife in the world, and she a Tzar's daughter.

From *Old Peter's Russian Tales* by Arthur Ransome (Thomas Nelson, London and New York)

(See Note, page 149)

The Story of
Epaminondas and his Auntie

EPAMINONDAS USED to go to see his Auntie 'most every day, and she nearly always gave him something to take home to his Mammy.

One day she gave him a big piece of cake; nice, yellow, rich gold-cake.

Epaminondas took it in his fist and held it all crunched up tight, like this, and came along home.

By the time he got home there wasn't anything left but a fistful of crumbs. His Mammy said,—

'What you got there, Epaminondas?'

'Cake, Mammy,' said Epaminondas.

'Cake!' said his Mammy. 'Epaminondas, you ain't got the sense you was born with!

' That's no way to carry cake. The way to carry cake is to wrap it all up nice in some leaves and put it in your hat, and put your hat on your head, and come along home.

'You hear me, Epaminondas?'

'Yes, Mammy,' said Epaminondas.

Next day Epaminondas went to see his Auntie, and she gave him a pound of butter for his Mammy; fine, fresh, sweet butter.

Epaminondas wrapped it up in leaves and put it in his hat, and put his hat on his head, and came along home. It was a very hot day.

Pretty soon the butter began to melt. It melted, and melted, and as it melted it ran down Epaminondas' forehead; then it ran over his face, and in his ears, and down his neck.

35

When he got home, all the butter Epaminondas had was *on him.*

His Mammy looked at him, and then she said,—

'Law's sake; Epaminondas, what you got in your hat?'

'Butter, Mammy,' said Epaminondas; 'Auntie gave it to me.

'Butter!' said his Mammy. 'Epaminondas, you ain't got the sense you was born with! Don't you know that's no way to carry butter?

'The way to carry butter is to wrap it up in some leaves and take it down to the brook, and cool it in the water, and cool it in the water, and cool it in the water, and then take it on your hands, careful, and bring it along home.'

'Yes, Mammy,' said Epaminondas.

By and by, another day, Epaminondas went to see his Auntie again, and this time she gave him a little new puppy-dog to take home.

Epaminondas put it in some leaves and took it down to the brook; and there he cooled it in the water, and cooled it in the water, and cooled it in the water; and then he took it in his hands and came along home.

When he got home, the puppy-dog was dead. His Mammy looked at it, and she said,—

'Law's sake! Epaminondas, what you got there?'

'A puppy-dog, Mammy,' said Epaminondas.

'A *puppy-dog*!' said his Mammy. 'My gracious sakes alive, Epaminondas, you ain't got the sense you was born with! That ain't the way to carry a puppy-dog!

'The way to carry a puppy-dog is to take a long piece of string and tie one end of it round the puppy-dog's neck and put the puppy-dog on the ground, and take hold of the other end of the string and come along home, like this.'

'All right, Mammy,' said Epaminondas.

Next day Epaminondas went to see his Auntie again, and when he came to go home she gave him a loaf of bread to carry to his Mammy; a brown, fresh, crusty loaf of bread.

So Epaminondas tied a string around the end of the loaf and took hold of the end of the string and came along home, like this.

When he got home his Mammy looked at the thing on the end of the string, and she said,—

'My laws a-massy! Epaminondas, what you got on the end of that string?'

'Bread, Mammy,' said Epaminondas; 'Auntie gave it to me.'

'Bread!!!' said his Mammy.
'O Epaminondas, Epaminondas, you ain't got the sense you was born with; you never did have the sense you was born with; you never will have the sense you was born with!

'Now I ain't gwine tell you any more ways to bring truck home. And don't you go see your Auntie, neither. I'll go see her my own self.

'But I'll just tell you one thing, Epaminondas! You see here these six mince pies I done make? You see how I done set 'em on the doorstep to cool?

'Well, now, you hear me, Epaminondas, *you be careful how you step on those pies!*'

'Yes, Mammy,' said Epaminondas.

Then Epaminondas' Mammy put on her bonnet and her shawl and took a basket in her hand and went away to see Auntie.

The six mince pies sat cooling in a row on the door-step.

And then,—and then,—Epaminondas *was* careful how he stepped on those pies!

He stepped—right—in—the middle—of—every—one.

And, do you know, children, nobody knows what happened

next! The person who told me the story didn't know; nobody knows. But you can guess.

From *Stories to Tell to Children* by Sara Cone Bryant (George G. Harrap, London; Houghton Mifflin, Boston)

(See Note, page 150)

The Story of
Brother Johannick and his Silver Bell

THIS IS a very old story—an ancient legend of Christmas-time—from Brittany, where it has been told and told again for many hundreds of years. It is the story of Brother Johannick and his silver bell.

It was long ago—five hundred years, or perhaps six hundred—that Brother Johannick lived, all alone on the tiny Isle Notre-Dame that lay midway in the wide estuary of the river Rance. At the mouth of the river is the port of St Malo. Inland were great forests, and there, all the year round, wood-cutters were busy; and cargoes of logs and faggots of wood were carried down the river to keep the fires burning that warmed the houses and cooked the food of the folk of St Malo. The logs were loaded on large heavy boats called *gabares*—the men who worked the boats were called *gabariers*. Up and down the river they sailed all through the year from the little town of Pludihen to the great port of St Malo.

It was in winter-time that the *gabariers* were most busy. Many loads of logs and many bundles of faggots were needed then to keep the hearths of St Malo burning. And it was in winter-time also that the boatmen were most grateful to Brother Johannick and his silver bell. For when days grew cold and nights were long the sea-fogs came rolling in from the Channel, spreading far and wide over the marshes so that no river banks, no houses, no landmarks could be seen. Then the wide mouth of the Rance was a dangerous place. There were strong tides and currents; there were sand-bars and mud-banks and little rocky islands. And in the thick grey fog no man could tell where his boat might be drifting unless there was something to steer by.

39

It was on those dark nights and days of cold, thick fog that Brother Johannick did his work. All night and all day while the fog lasted he stood by the shore of Isle Notre-Dame and rang his silver bell. The clear ringing sound floated out across the water and *gabariers* would listen and say: 'Ah! there I hear Brother Johannick's bell. Steer a little farther to the right. I can tell by the sound that we are too near the shore.' Or: 'Listen—there is the bell. We are drawing near Isle Notre-Dame—be careful of the current, there is a rock hereabouts.' And they blessed Brother Johannick for his goodness and his care.

They did what they could to show they were grateful to him. On clear days and nights as the *gabares* passed the island, the boatmen would drop a big log or a good faggot of wood overboard just where the current would carry it safely and surely to the shore of Isle Notre-Dame. Brother Johannick thankfully dragged the wood to land and piled it by his shelter, and in his turn he blessed the *gabariers* for their warm hearts and kind thought for him.

The years went by and Brother Johannick grew old. His long white beard hung down over his brown robe. His back was bent and he went slowly. It was not so easy for him to wade into deep water and to pull in heavy logs and faggots. So the pile of wood by his shelter was smaller and his fire was not so warm nor so comforting. But his heart was brave, and still day by day and night by night when storms came and darkness and thick sea-fogs, Brother Johannick never failed to ring his silver bell.

Then there came a year when it turned bitterly cold just a week before Christmas. There was hard frost each night; the stones of the island were white with it, and where the little spring trickled down, great icicles hung from the rocks. With the frost came a thick white fog. It never lifted; day after day it covered the marshes, the river and the island. And by day and by night, Brother Johannick rang his silver bell.

Christmas Eve came. His fire had gone out. He had no more

logs. His old brown robe was thin and ragged and damp with mist. He was shivering and very weary. But he sang Christmas hymns as he rang his bell and his heart was warm with joy and gratefulness as he thought of the love of God that brought Christ Jesus to the manger at Bethlehem with the message of love to men.

The hours of the night went by and presently he stopped his ringing. 'Midnight is surely passed,' he said. 'I must kneel a moment to say a prayer, for Christmas Day is here.' And he knelt down upon the shore to say 'Our Father.' He could scarcely kneel, he was so weary and so stiff with cold; and when he came to the end of his prayer his voice was only a whisper and he did not rise from his knees. His tired old head nodded forward; Brother Johannick gave a little sigh and slipped down and lay fast asleep beside the ashes of his fire.

In the little town of Pludihen on the Rance, the fog was thick too that Christmas Eve. But the houses were warm. Every hearth had its great Christmas log; there was plenty of wood in the forests for all.

Père Suliac the *gabarier* sat warming himself by the blaze. He was very comfortable and his wife was cooking something that smelled very good in the pot that hung over the fire.

But Père Suliac was not quite happy in his mind. He fidgeted, and every now and then he went to the window and opened the wooden shutter and looked out into the fog and listened. 'I am thinking of Brother Johannick,' he said when his wife asked what troubled him. 'He must be cold on that island of his, and I am wondering what he is doing about a fire. With this fog he will not manage to find many logs floating in the water. I have a good mind,' said Père Suliac suddenly, 'to take him some wood this very night, to give him a fire for Christmas. He does enough for us out there in the dark and the cold; one should do something for him.'

But Mère Suliac was frightened. 'Why should you go out so late on such a night?' she said crossly. 'Brother Johannick

2*

stays on the island of his own free will. Nobody makes him do it. Stay and be warm by your fire this Christmas Eve.'

Père Suliac said no more, but he thought to himself: 'The holy man shall have a log for Christmas, all the same.'

Very late that night—it was past midnight—Père Suliac sat up in his bed and listened for the silver bell. Mère Suliac lay fast asleep, but he had only closed his eyes and pretended he was sleeping. He had a plan to carry out as soon as all was quiet in the house.

'There is no sound of the bell,' he said to himself. 'What can have happened? It was ringing well enough a while ago.'

He listened again. 'No—there it is after all, and how strong and clear it sounds. Surely the good God gives strength to the holy man's arm!'

He slipped quietly out of bed in the dark and felt about for his clothes. But they were not there! Then he laughed a little to himself. 'The good wife has hidden my clothes while my eyes were shut,' he said. 'She guessed what I meant to do and she thought she would stop me. But there is the old sheepskin coat hanging by the door and that will do well enough. There is no one to see that I am only half dressed, in this fog, and the holy man will not mind!'

He belted the old coat round him and slipped out barefoot down to the river where his boat was moored; there was a good pile of logs and some faggots on board. He hoisted his sails; there was just a breath of wind, and with the current it would carry him straight to Isle Notre-Dame. And it was easy to steer, in spite of fog and darkness, for never had he heard the bell ring so sweet and clear.

But it was not only the bell that guided him; a light was shining through the mist. Père Suliac looked and looked again. 'One would say there was moonlight somewhere,' he said. 'But there is no moon to-night.'

Presently he saw that the light must come from Isle Notre-Dame. It was not a red glow such as a fire would give; it shone silver bright. The fog was turned to a shining mist and from the mist the bell rang sweet and clear.

Père Suliac was puzzled and almost afraid. 'This is the time of Christmas,' he said, 'when angels sang songs upon earth and surely this is a heavenly light. Perhaps the angels themselves are upon Isle Notre-Dame.' And then he remembered that he was wearing nothing but the old sheepskin coat. He was troubled as he thought of it.

'Certainly,' said Père Suliac, 'it is not suitable or respect-able that I should come before the angels dressed like this.' And with his knife he slit a long strip from his mainsail and wrapped it round himself under his coat like a kind of kilt and tied it with a piece of cord.

'There!' he said, looking at himself with satisfaction. 'Now I am more properly clothed.'

And then, suddenly, the boat came out of the mist into a little clear space of water. In the midst was Isle Notre-Dame; all round the fog lay like a shining wall but overhead the stars were clear. The light came from the island—a soft clear shining light, so that Père Suliac could see Brother Johannick, very old and weary, lying fast asleep upon the cold white frosty ground by the ashes of a burned-out fire. But beside Brother Johannick there stood a little Child all in white, and in his hand the Child held the silver bell, ringing it steadily and sweetly so that the sound floated far across the river and the wide marshlands beyond.

The boat drifted gently on the bright water, and when it came near the shore the Child put out a little hand and beckoned. Père Suliac made the boat fast and waded to the shore with a great log and an armful of faggots. Then he knelt down and laid the wood at the feet of the little Child and bowed his head. And the Child smiled and laid a hand on Père Suliac's head and then on the wood, blessing both.

It seemed to Père Suliac then that all the Isle Notre-Dame was full of the songs of angels with a wonderful feeling of loving-kindness and of joy all around; and in his mind he said:

'This is no angel; this is the heavenly Christ-Child.' And a light sprang up so clear and dazzling that he closed his eyes.

When he looked again the light had gone. There was only the bare little island sparkling with frost in the starlight. But the night was clear and on the cold black ashes of Brother Johannick's fire, where he had laid the wood, bright flames were darting and crackling. The Christmas log was alight and

blazing; and beside the fire Brother Johannick was awaking and the silver bell was in his hand.

Père Suliac told him all that he had seen; and Brother Johannick said: 'Most surely it was the Christ-Child.' And they knelt down together to give thanks for Christmas Day and for all the love of God that Christ Jesus showed to men.

Then Père Suliac landed his load of wood and when morning came he sailed back in the sunshine across the water to Pludihen.

Some of the men by the waterside laughed when they saw Père Suliac so oddly dressed in his sheepskin coat and his sailcloth kilt. But they did not laugh when they heard his story. They were glad and grateful to Brother Johannick for all his patient watchfulness, to Père Suliac for his kindness, and most of all they gave thanks to our Father in Heaven, who sends Christ-love to the hearts of men.

And the old story tells them that henceforward the *gabariers* of Pludihen dressed themselves as Père Suliac was dressed that Christmas Eve, in coat and sailcloth kilt, that they might keep in memory all that had happened on that most wonderful night.

From *Tales for Jack and Jane* by Elizabeth Clark (University of London Press, London)

(See Note, page 151)

Volkh's Journey to the East

ABOUT TWO miles to the east of Kiev in a small timbered house by the shore of a lake lived a widowed gentlewoman called Martha and her only son, Volkh.

Martha was poor, and she could not afford to buy any of those things which were enjoyed by boys of Volkh's age—green leather boots, coats of scarlet cloth, a sable cap, a horse, and a really good bow. Volkh ran barefoot, he wore rough smocks in the summer and sheepskins in the winter, had a bow made of withies, and rode a shaggy little pony which was as stubborn as a donkey.

Volkh did not know that his mother had a rare jewel hidden away in the chest in the back room of the house. It was an emerald buckle given to Martha on her wedding-day by her godmother, a wise old woman.

'There is great virtue in the buckle,' she had said then. 'It is neither for wearing nor for selling. Keep it hidden until the day when someone asks for it, and it will cost you dear to part with it, but you must do so.'

'How can anyone ask for it when nobody will ever know I have got it, and why should I have to give it up?' Martha had asked, but the old woman would not tell her, and soon after she died.

Now Volkh, who could not remember his father, grumbled often enough about the poor way they lived. He longed for a smart scarlet coat and a bow made of good Norwegian yew. He grumbled about the wooden trenchers and cups they used at table. He sometimes longed for roast goose and sturgeon for dinner, and Martha could not always afford enough money for the porridge. And many a time she secretly wished that she might take the emerald buckle to Kiev, sell it to some foreign

46

merchant, and come home, laden with many things for her son's enjoyment, but she dared not break her godmother's wish.

So Volkh passed his twelfth birthday. He had good skill with his bow, and, being of noble birth, he could be sent to Kiev to join the Prince's household, but Martha knew that she could never afford to equip him for such service. She did not quite know what future awaited him, and she tried not to worry too much. In spite of all his frequent bouts of discontent, Volkh was a good son, and on many occasions Martha was proud of his courage. Volkh was not afraid to wander off into the neighbouring woods, and he always came back with something for the larder in his pouch, and he was very clever with his fishing rods.

One summer morning Martha was combing her hair by the window when she heard a great noise outside the gate. Her first thought was that Volkh, who had gone out at dawn, had been killed by a bear. Martha hid her hair under a linen coif and ran down the carved wooden stairway as fast as her trembling legs would carry her.

At once she breathed in deep relief. Her son stood there, his wet smock gloving his body, his hair, legs and arms all covered with weeds, and by the side of him was an elderly man, dripping from head to foot, his pilgrim's cloak torn and muddy. There was a small crowd behind them—all shouting and clapping. The old pilgrim had fallen into the lake and Volkh had jumped in and pulled him out.

When things were somewhat quieter, Martha told her maid to get some dry clothing and to set the table for a meal. She offered broiled fish and a rye loaf with apologies for such a scant breakfast, but the old pilgrim said courteously:

'Madam, I am not used to rich fare.'

When they had eaten, Volkh ran away to look for the fishing-rod he had mislaid, and the pilgrim said:

'Madam, you are known to me though I am a stranger to you. When I was in Jerusalem I had a command given me to come and see you on my return to Rus.'

'Who gave it to you?' asked Martha quickly, but the old man did not answer the question and went on:

'You had an emerald buckle given to you on your wedding-day and I am here to ask for it.'

Martha said sadly:

'This is a very poor manor, and I had always hoped that nobody would come for the buckle whilst I was alive so that my son might have something for his future,' and she sighed, tears welling up in her eyes.

'Your son will never lack for anything,' the pilgrim said gently, but Martha shook her head. She thought that the old man would probably offer the buckle at some shrine along his way. It certainly seemed unfair, but there was nothing to be done. She got up and went into the back room and returned, a small lime-wood box in her hands.

'I'd much rather not look at it again.' Martha laid the box on the table. 'May God's blessing be your companion all along the way.'

The pilgrim bowed and hid the box in the folds of his smock. Martha never watched him leave the room—her eyes were all misted with tears. She just did not know what she could do about Volkh's future. She never knew how long she had sat by the table when his excited voice roused her.

'Mother! Mother! Look! I have found it all by the lake shore and everything fits me.'

Martha raised her head and remained at gaze. Volkh stood there, a magnificent hauberk of Damascene mesh mail on him. He wore beautiful white linen breeches and green boots with silver tassels. There was a bright red plume on his helmet, and his hands, gloved in stout buff leather, held a short pike and an axe.

'Son,' Martha gasped at last. 'Am I awake or asleep? You look like a Knight of the Golden Table!'

'No, Mother, because there was no shield among the things,' Volkh replied.

'But who gave you these wonderful things?'

'The pilgrim. I saw him leave the house, make for the lake shore, and stand there some time, and then I saw the things appear one by one—so quickly, too, it seemed as though they came either from the air or from the ground. I ran as fast as I could. I thought it was all a dream. He waved his hand, said they were all for me, and vanished. Here is a piece of writing.'

Neither Martha nor Volkh knew their letters. They took the small piece of parchment to the parish clerk who read out:

'Six wishes for Volkh. Three wishes for Prince Danilo. There is no tenth wish.'

'Why, that means that I must ride to Kiev at once,' cried Volkh, 'and ask the little Prince what his wishes are.'

'God protect you along the way,' said the parish clerk severely—he had not seen the pilgrim and rather doubted the story told him by Martha.

Mother and son turned homewards. She said:

'Volkh, I am afraid that it is a far distance for that old pony of yours, and some of the going is rough.'

'Oh, I wish I had a horse to take me to the very gates of Kiev within an instant,' cried the boy, and the very next instant he was in the saddle, a beautiful black horse under him, and he was no longer at the gate of his mother's house. There stood the great turreted walls of Kiev. Beyond, domes, cupolas and roofs blended into a marvellous tapestry of gold, crimson, blue and green. Yet no bells could be heard, and the watch at the gates were sobbing bitterly. Volkh leapt out of the saddle.

'Oh, what has happened?' he asked.

'It is our little Prince Danilo,' gulped one of the men. 'Yesterday he rode out with his falcon, and he had his body-guard, too, but he was kidnapped by an enemy from a very far country—they say they are all magicians there, and one of their men shot an arrow into the city with a message for the Prince. I cannot rightly tell you what was in it, but all the Knights of the Golden Table left Kiev within a few minutes.

Not one of them has yet returned. Well, young sir, ride on into the city!'

Volkh had heard so much of the crowds, the markets, the gaiety of life in Kiev. He found it a city of mourning. Nobody was to be seen in the streets, and all the shops were closed and the markets empty. The people crowded the Cathedral and all the churches to pray for the rescue of their little Prince, Vladimir's only son and heir. Volkh rode on to the gateway of the palace. He knew well that he had the right to ask to see his sovereign and now he understood why his knightly gear had been given him. Volkh felt very excited and not a little scared. He also remembered that he must be very careful about wishing. He had already expressed a wish for a horse. Five wishes only were left to him.

According to custom Volkh took off his helmet and belt

when he reached the porch of the palace. The captain of the men-at-arms asked his name and added:

'Prince Vladimir will not refuse to see you, but have you some really urgent business? He is in great distress.'

Volkh replied, his words a surprise to himself:

'I am here to ask for the Prince's blessing. I mean to rescue the little Prince.'

The man stared very hard and pulled at his beard.

'Prince Vladimir is in no mood for such unkind jokes, boy. You don't look old enough to carry a sword.'

'I am sorry. I had to leave it in the porch together with my helmet and belt. I wish I had it on me to prove—' and Volkh stopped because the belt, the sword dangling from it, was round his waist in an instant.

'Four wishes left,' gasped Volkh. 'Really, I must be careful.'

The captain of the men-at-arms was shaking from head to foot.

'Take it off, take it off at once, and tell it to stay where you put it, and you are not to scare Prince Vladimir the way you scared me.'

Presently Volkh was led into the crimson painted hall, and the Prince received him kindly enough.

'Have you come to ask me to right some injustice, son?' he asked.

'No, my lord,' Volkh replied. 'I have come for your blessing,' and he knelt, the tips of his fingers touching the edge of the golden table. 'I mean to ride and rescue the young Prince.'

Vladimir stared.

'You have no idea what you are talking about! He has been taken to a country called Persia—and they flew away with him. His bodyguard saw it happen. All Persians are great magicians, and the Shah of Persia has asked for a ransom— ten thousand white heifers without a blemish. All the Knights of the Golden Table have ridden to look for them. I doubt if they will find as many hundred,' and Prince Vladimir sat very still. He thought of his wife, Princess Eupraxia, weeping in her room upstairs.

'I have not got a single white heifer to offer, my lord,' said Volkh, 'but it is my duty to go,' and he told Vladimir about the pilgrim's visit, the miraculous gift of equipment and horse, and the little piece of parchment.

'It is my duty to go, my lord,' he said again, and Prince Vladimir raised his right hand.

'God bless you, my son, and He alone can protect you. The hazards are far more than you think.'

Volkh rose, bowed, and murmured:

'Oh, I wish I were in the saddle and at the place where the young Prince is!'

No sooner had he said it than he found himself in a strange mountainous country. He sat in the saddle, facing a cleft be-

tween two huge rocks. To the left of him stretched a valley
with innumerable white tents. To the right of him, he saw
four huge poles so tall that he could hardly see their tops
where two criss-cross poles were joined together, and from the
middle swung an enormous gilt cage—most sumptuously
furnished with cushions and coverlets of white velvet and
violet silk, and there sat little Prince Danilo dressed in a pink
and green striped Persian robe, with a Persian cap on his
head. The very sight of these clothes infuriated Volkh. How
dared they put them on a prince of Kiev?

The child raised his head, and Volkh saw that he had been
crying.

'I am from Kiev, Prince Danilo,' said Volkh and jumped
out of the saddle. 'I have come to take you home.'

The little Prince stood up and clung to the bars.

'You mustn't come too near,' he cried. 'A kindly Persian
woman tried to give me some food, and two huge hounds ran
from behind a rock as soon as she touched the bars, and they
killed her.'

Volkh unsheathed his sword.

'I expect I could deal with those hounds, Prince Danilo, but
before I get any nearer, please tell me how the cage opens. The
bars go all the way round and there doesn't seem to be a lock
anywhere.'

'They welded the bars together,' sobbed the little Prince.
'They said my dear father would never get ten thousand white
heifers for my ransom and that I would never come out. Oh
dear, I am so hungry and thirsty, too!'

'Keep in good heart, Prince Danilo.' Volkh rode nearer and
stretched out his hands towards the bars. At once two
enormous hounds, fangs bared, sprang from behind a rock.

'I wish both of you were dead within an instant,' cried
Volkh, and down they went at once.

'I have just three wishes left,' he thought, 'that is—three
for myself. Wasn't there something about three wishes for
Prince Danilo? I must find out,' and he said aloud: 'Well, one

hurdle is behind us, and don't worry—I mean to get you out, but don't you wish you could have some food before the journey home?'

'Food?' echoed the little Prince. 'I wish I had a stale crust to chew!'

Volkh watched narrowly, but no stale crust appeared on the white velvet cushions.

'The spell must work differently for the little Prince,' he thought. 'And I have three wishes of my own left now. One for the cage to open, one for some food, and the third for the speedy return to Kiev. Now then,' Volkh took a deep breath and said: 'I wish the cage would open,' and at once the bars fell apart and the little Prince jumped down, right into Volkh's arms.

'Steady, Prince,' said Volkh. 'Now you must not ride hungry,' and again he spoke the words, and there was a table covered with a white cloth and laden with dishes; fragrant sturgeon soup, mushroom pies, roast fowl, honey-bread and milk in a silver jug, and Prince Danilo urged Volkh to share all the good things with him. When they had eaten, Volkh said:

'Now for home,' and he was just about to lift the little Prince into the saddle when Danilo said sadly:

'These dreadful outlandish clothes! My father's people would think I had turned Persian! Oh for my little blue coat and my green boots with tassels!'

'Yes,' Volkh nodded sympathetically, 'I wish I could bring you home in those clothes,' and there stood the Prince in his blue coat and white shirt, its collar worked in red cross-stitch, and the high green boots.

'You are a very good magician.' The child clapped his hands for pleasure, but Volkh's face had gone white. He had spent the last wish.

'I suppose we had better hurry,' said the boy, and Volkh lifted him into the saddle.

Volkh's heart was beating wildly. If he turned the horse

south, he would ride straight into the Persian camp. If he rode north, he might lose his way in the mountains. How far were they from Kiev? He could not tell, but he felt sure it was a fearful distance.

'Has your horse gone lame?' Prince Danilo asked politely, turned his head, and screamed. 'Look, they are going to chase us—'

It was true. Volkh spurred the horse and plunged into the rocky pass. He had spent his last wish, but at least he had a wonderful mount to ride, and the black horse flew like an eagle. Soon their pursuers were left far behind, but Volkh's horse was still galloping through the wild rocky country. For all Volkh knew, they were going farther and farther from Kiev, and he knew the sun was about to set. What could he do? The little paper mentioned three wishes for Prince Danilo, but the boy asked for food, and no food had come. . . .

He reined in the horse on a narrow rocky shelf, and dismounted. Suddenly he felt so tired that he would have given all he had for an hour's sleep. The little Prince, still in the saddle, looked down and said softly:

'I suppose we are still far away from Kiev. I wish you were not so tired,' and no sooner had the child spoken than Volkh felt his fatigue slipping away. In fact, he thought he would have enough strength to cleave a rock in two. So here lay the key: the little Prince's wishes worked so long as they did not concern himself. And there were only two of them left. Volkh caught his breath.

'Well, we have ridden a good distance, and we cannot be very far away from Kiev—'

And he was about to mount when Danilo bent down and touched his shoulders.

'Oh, I wish you would not look so sad!'

And instantly Volkh was feeling as happy as he had never felt before—just when there was nothing for him to feel happy about. Then he had an idea, and he staked Danilo's last wish on it. If it failed, they were lost, 'and we must not fail,' thought Volkh stubbornly.

So he leapt into the saddle and said:

'I am sorry, Prince Danilo. I was thinking of my mother. She did not know that I would be coming here. She expected me home quite soon,' and having said it, Volkh prayed with all his might that the little Prince would answer in the right way.

Danilo said nothing for a moment. Then he whispered:

'Yes, I understand. I wish your mother could see you riding through the streets of Kiev!'

At once the grim rocks were gone. They were riding very slowly down the street of Wisdom, and Volkh's eyes caught Martha's happy proud face as she stood at the edge of the square. They rode on to the sound of bells and deafening cheers. Vladimir and Eupraxia rushed past the guard to greet them.

A little later Volkh and Martha were summoned into the crimson hall. All the Knights were still away looking for the white heifers for the Prince's ransom, but another oaken chair had been added to the others, and a small red-plumed helmet lay on the table in token of a Knight's presence in the palace. Martha burst into tears of joy, but Volkh stammered that he was not fit to be a Knight.

'But that is for your sovereign to say,' Vladimir told him and, bending forward, touched the boy's right shoulder.

From *The Knights of the Golden Table* by E. M. Almedingen (Bodley Head, London; J. B. Lippincott, New York)

(See Note, page 152)

Did you Feed my Cow?

Make motions suggested by the response.

CALL   Did you feed my cow?
RESPONSE   *Yes, ma'am!*
Will you tell me how?
    Yes, ma'am!
Oh, what did you give her?
    Corn and hay.
Oh, what did you give her?
    Corn and hay.

Did you milk her good?
    Yes, ma'am!
Did you do like you should?
    Yes, ma'am!
Oh, how did you milk her?
    Swish! Swish! Swish!
Oh, how did you milk her?
    Swish! Swish! Swish!

Did my cow die?
    Yes, ma'am!
Did my cow die?
    Yes, ma'am!
Oh, how did she die?
    Ugh! Ugh! Ugh!
Oh, how did she die?
    Ugh! Ugh! Ugh!

Did the buzzards come?
Yes, ma'am!
For to pick her bones?
Yes, ma'am!
Oh, how did they come?
Flop! Flop! Flop!
Oh, how did they come?
Flop! Flop! Flop!

From *Did you Feed my Cow?* by Margaret Taylor (Thomas Y. Crowell, New York)

(See Note, page 153)

Bertha Goldfoot

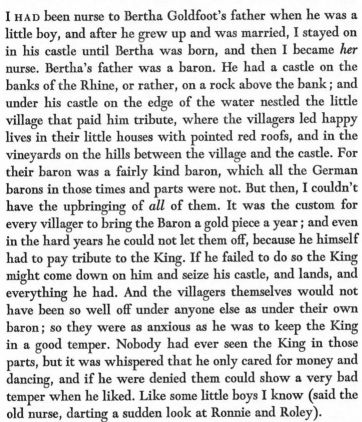

I HAD been nurse to Bertha Goldfoot's father when he was a little boy, and after he grew up and was married, I stayed on in his castle until Bertha was born, and then I became *her* nurse. Bertha's father was a baron. He had a castle on the banks of the Rhine, or rather, on a rock above the bank; and under his castle on the edge of the water nestled the little village that paid him tribute, where the villagers led happy lives in their little houses with pointed red roofs, and in the vineyards on the hills between the village and the castle. For their baron was a fairly kind baron, which all the German barons in those times and parts were not. But then, I couldn't have the upbringing of *all* of them. It was the custom for every villager to bring the Baron a gold piece a year; and even in the hard years he could not let them off, because he himself had to pay tribute to the King. If he failed to do so the King might come down on him and seize his castle, and lands, and everything he had. And the villagers themselves would not have been so well off under anyone else as under their own baron; so they were as anxious as he was to keep the King in a good temper. Nobody had ever seen the King in those parts, but it was whispered that he only cared for money and dancing, and if he were denied them could show a very bad temper when he liked. Like some little boys I know (said the old nurse, darting a sudden look at Ronnie and Roley).

When Bertha was born, there was a christening, of course, and all the noblemen and noblewomen of the countryside came to it, and also, of course, all the chief fairies. The Baron and his wife tried to remember every fairy of importance, for they knew something bad might happen to their child if one was forgotten. They even invited the Lorelei, the lovely water-nymph who sits and sings on a rock in the middle of the Rhine, and with her magic song draws men to their death. Many a friend of the Baron had been drowned at the foot of the Lorelei's rock, but the Baron did not dare leave her out, all the same. She did not appear, however, until the feast was over, and everybody had presented his gift and departed. Then, as the Baron and his wife and I were alone with little Bertha in her cradle, the doors of the great hall swung open, and the lovely Lorelei glided in, with her mantle of golden hair flowing about her like the golden waters of the Rhine. And like the river, it was wet, and so were her green gar-ments, and her white skin. She stepped up to the cradle, and leaning over touched the baby's right foot with her wet finger, saying,

'Child, men shall call you Bertha Goldfoot. The Lorelei gives you a foot of gold from the day you are able to walk.'

Then she glided out of the hall, leaving a trail of water on the floor behind her. And none of us knew what she meant by her gift. While we were wondering, we heard a horrid little chuckle, and up through the floor popped Rumpelstiltskin, the Stocking-Elf. Everyone knows what a nasty little creature *he* is, and the Baron had not even thought of inviting him to the christening, because he is not of any great importance in the fairy world. Even if he was offended, it was not in his power to do very much harm, but we all felt uneasy as he hopped over to the cradle, and pointed his finger at Bertha's left foot.

'Child,' he croaked, 'you shall always have a hole in your left stocking as long as you live. That's what Rumpelstiltskin gives you for a christening-gift!'

With that he disappeared as suddenly as he had come. The Baron said, 'It's bad enough, but it might have been much worse'; but I myself wasn't so sure, for it's the little things that matter most. And the Baron's wife said, 'For my part, I think the Lorelei's gift was the worse of the two. If the child grows up with a gold foot, how shall we ever get her married? Nobody would want a wife with such an oddity about her.'

'We must keep her foot covered up all the time, so that nobody shall guess,' said the Baron. 'See to it for us, Nanny,' he added, turning to me. 'Luckily the guests have all gone, and the three of us can keep Bertha's gold foot a secret between us until she is married.'

The first year of the baby's life, I spent all my spare time in knitting stockings for her, against the day when she would be able to walk; for it was then that she was to get her gold foot. The first time I saw her totter on to her little feet, to try to run from me to her mother, I caught the child up, and pulled on her stockings, so that the whole of her feet and ankles were covered; for if a maid or a page had happened to catch a glimpse of the golden foot, the story would travel through the land. Then we let little Bertha begin to toddle as she pleased; but from that day she wore no more socks, because socks can slip down to the ankle—as Mary Matilda knows!

Bertha even had to sleep in her stockings; and I was careful always to change them at night in the dark, so that even I never saw her right foot after she was one year old. Her left foot, on the other hand, everybody saw; at least, they saw a part of it. For almost as soon as her left stocking was on, a big hole came in the heel like magic. It was no use scolding her, or watching to see how it happened—there the hole was! At first I would change the stocking at once, but five minutes later I had to change it again, and at last I said to the Baron and his wife, 'It's no manner of good, my dears. We can't keep the holes from coming, so the child will have to wear boots.' And from the time she was about two, Bertha did. It wasn't very pleasant for her to have to wear boots from morning to night, no matter what she was doing, but it couldn't be helped. Boots she wore, from her babyhood to her eighteenth birthday, when she was as beautiful a young woman as any baron's daughter on the Rhine. Moreover, everybody loved her, from her parents to the barefoot boat-boy in the village, with whom she had often played in her childhood. As she grew older, suitors for her hand began to present themselves, but she cared for none of them.

Now this year was, as it happened, a terribly bad one for the vine-harvest. The blight had got into it somehow; the grapes rotted, and the peasants in the village were as poor as church mice in consequence. At the end of the season they came weeping to the castle door and asked audience of the Baron.

'My lord,' said the chief Vine-grower, 'our hearts are broken and our pockets too. We cannot pay you the tribute this year.'

'If you do not,' said the Baron, 'both you and I will be ruined. For the bad year has hit me as well as you, and if I do not pay him the King will descend on us in wrath.'

'My lord,' said the peasants, 'our children are starving, and we have nothing left. We would pay you gladly if we could; but who can pay what he has not got?'

The Baron was very angry, for he was not always a reasonable man; and kind as he really was, he was prepared to punish them, when Bertha, who was sitting at his feet, looked up at him saying, 'They cannot help it, Father. Let us hope for the best, and heaven will soften the King's heart or will send us the means to pay him.'

Her smile was so sweet that the Baron could not resist it, and he said to the peasant, 'Well, then, whatever bad fortune may fall upon us, we will share it together.' And the peasants returned to the village, thanking him and blessing his daughter.

But heaven did not soften the King's heart. He came riding in wrath, with his soldiers behind him, to demand the reason why the Baron had not paid him the tribute. The Baron pointed out to him the blighted vines, saying, 'There, sire, lies all my fortune, in ruins. The grapes were my gold, and gave me the gold I gave you.'

'And gold I will have!' said the King. 'I care not for your reasons. If you cannot pay me, I will take your castle, your village, and all you possess.'

As he spoke, Bertha came into the hall. Her mother and I
had dressed her in a gown of white silk, and crowned her head
with her golden plaits, hoping that her beauty might win the
King's heart, and save the day. Indeed, he stood amazed with
admiration, as I knew he would, and turning to the Baron
said, 'Who is this maiden?'

'My daughter, sire,' he answered.

'In that case, Baron,' said the King, 'I will marry your
daughter, and her wedding-portion shall be the debt you owe
me.'

I could see that the Baron was overjoyed, and so was his
wife. Bertha, poor child, turned as pale as her gown, and cast
down her eyes before the King, who was admiring her from
top to toe. But when his gaze *did* reach her toes, he frowned
a little, and asked, 'Why does she wear boots?'

The Baron stammered hastily, 'She has been out walking,
and has only just come in.'

'Put on your shoes,' said the King to Bertha, 'for I would
like to see how my bride can dance.'

'I have no shoes, Your Majesty,' said Bertha; and this was
true—she had never had a pair of shoes since she was a baby.

'Then I will dance with you in your stocking-feet,' said the
King. And it was no use protesting. Bertha had to take off her
boots before him, and there, in the heel of her left stocking,
was an enormous hole. The King looked surprised, and bade
her go and change her stockings. But what was the use? She
came back with a hole as big as before. A third time she tried,
and still her rosy left heel was bare to everybody's view, and
her cheeks were rosier still, as she hung her head and
blushed for shame.

The King's admiration now turned to scorn, and he said to
the Baron, 'Beautiful as your daughter is, I cannot have a
slattern for my queen. Farewell; but if the money is not paid
by to-morrow, I will turn you out of your castle.' So saying,
he rode away.

The Baron now turned in anger on his daughter. 'It is you,

with your wretched gift, who have brought me to this!' he cried. 'You are not fit to be my daughter, you slattern! Go away from my castle for ever, but go barefoot. It is better for the world to see your gold foot at last, than to see you with a hole in your stocking.'

He himself pulled off her stockings; and when he uncovered her right foot, lo and behold! it was as white as her

left. It surprised us all, for if Bertha's foot was not gold, what did the Lorelei mean by the gift? But the Baron was in too much of a rage to care about this; he lifted her in his arms and bore her down to the village, crying, 'My peasants, thanks to my daughter, I am now a beggar like yourselves. Who wants a beggar's daughter for his wife?'

While the people stood round amazed, the barefooted boat-boy, whom Bertha had played with as a child, stepped

forward and said modestly, 'I want her, my lord, if she will
have me.' And Bertha nodded her golden head, and the Baron,
with a harsh laugh, gave her into the boy's arms and strode
away. The boy called to the priest to ring the wedding-bell at
once, and set Bertha down on the ground; and for the first
time since she was a year old, Bertha's bare foot touched the
earth, and they walked to church together. But here is the

strange thing. Wherever her right foot stepped, it left behind
it a piece of gold. So that the whole of her way into church
and out again was marked by a double line of shining coins.
And the people following after cried in astonishment, 'Bertha
Goldfoot! Look, there goes Bertha Goldfoot!' So it was for
the rest of the day; the fiddler and piper struck up for the
wedding-dance, and the people danced in their shoes, with
the barefoot bride and groom in their midst. And wherever
3+

Bertha danced, the gold danced under her very toes. By midnight there was so much gold on the ground that the peasants were kept busy sweeping it up; and in the morning they carried it in a sack to the Baron and said, 'Here is our tribute, my lord. The village is saved.'

The Baron was now as joyful as he had been angry; he sent the gold post-haste to the King, and asked how it had all come about. And when he heard that it was all due to the wonderful gift of his own daughter, he hastened down to the village and forgave her.

'Come back to the castle with me, my darling child!' he said.

But Bertha shook her golden head and laughed. 'I cannot, Father. I am married now, and must live with my husband. Besides,' said she, 'I can never wear stockings again, for my gold foot loses its power unless it goes bare. But neither you nor the peasants need fear poverty any more.'

Her father embraced her, and saw that it must be so. And from then to the end of her days, Bertha and her husband, and all their children, too, lived barefoot.

From *The Old Nurse's Stocking Basket* by Eleanor Farjeon (University of London Press, London)

(See Note, page 153)

The Golden Phoenix

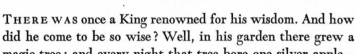

THERE WAS once a King renowned for his wisdom. And how did he come to be so wise? Well, in his garden there grew a magic tree; and every night that tree bore one silver apple— the apple of wisdom. Each morning the King would take it from the tree and eat it while the trumpets blew. As a result he governed wisely and well, and all his people lived happily.

Then a strange thing happened. One morning, when the King came to pick the apple, it was gone. No one saw it go; and no one admitted to taking it.

'Someone has stolen the silver apple,' said the King grimly. The next night he set his royal guards about the tree to keep watch.

But to no avail. In the evening the silver apple was there, ripening on its branch; in the morning it had gone. The guards swore that no one had passed them during the night.

The King called his three sons to him.

'This is a serious matter,' he said. 'Someone is stealing the silver apple during the night, and not even my royal guards can catch him. My sons, I put the task in your hands. Whichever of you succeeds in catching the thief will be rewarded with my crown and my kingdom.'

'I will stand guard to-night,' promised the eldest prince.

That evening he went into the garden and prepared to spend the night at the foot of the tree. He took a bottle of wine to keep himself company. From time to time he poured himself a cupful and gulped it down. Then as midnight drew near, he began to yawn.

'I must not fall asleep,' he told himself. And he got up and marched around the tree. He could see the silver apple gleaming in the moonlight.

But soon he was too tired to go on walking. Surely it would do no harm to sit down for a moment? He sat down. Pop! He fell asleep.

When he woke, the damage was done. The silver apple had vanished.

'Well,' he said, 'good-bye to the crown!'

Next morning the King asked for news of the thief, and of course there was no news. The eldest prince had gone to sleep at his post.

'Leave it to me, Father,' said the second prince. 'I'll catch your thief.'

The King shook his head doubtfully. But next evening the second prince went into the garden and prepared to spend the night at the foot of the tree. He took a platter of food to keep himself company. He felt sure that cold chicken and potato salad would keep him awake. But as midnight drew near he began to yawn.

'No one is going to bewitch me into falling asleep,' he told himself. And he got up and marched around the tree. The apple was still there, gleaming in the moonlight.

But soon he was too tired to go on walking. Surely it would do no harm to sit down for a moment? He sat down. Pop! He fell asleep.

When he woke an hour later he jumped to his feet. But the damage was done. The silver apple had vanished.

'Well, that's that,' he said. 'I too have lost the crown.'

Next morning the King asked if he had had better luck than his brother.

'No, Father,' said the second prince, ashamed. 'I stayed awake till midnight. But when midnight struck, I was sleeping like a badger.'

Petit Jean, the youngest prince, burst out laughing. 'A fine pair of sentries you are!'

'It's easy for you to talk,' said his brother crossly. 'You were sound asleep in your bed.'

'All the same, if the King my father sends me to stand

guard, *I* will bring back news of how the apple disappears.'

'My dear son,' said the King. 'This is no ordinary thief. How can you be so sure you'll do better than your brothers?'

'Well,' said Petit Jean, 'I'm sure I can do no worse.'

And so next evening he went into the garden and prepared to spend the night there. He looked up at the silver apple, gleaming by the light of the moon. Then he sat down to wait. When he felt himself growing sleepy, he got up and marched around the tree. But as midnight drew near, he began to yawn.

'This will never do,' he told himself. 'If I fall asleep, the apple will disappear as usual—and how my brothers will laugh!'

He climbed into the tree and settled himself in a forked branch near the magic fruit. Then he put out his hand to the apple. It was as smooth as ivory, and as cool as the night.

'Suppose I picked it now,' he thought. 'Then no one would be able to steal it without my noticing.'

He plucked the apple from the branch and put it inside his shirt. Then he tucked in his shirt and buttoned it right up to the neck. Not a moment too soon. Pop! His eyes closed and he fell sound asleep.

But he was waked almost at once by something pulling at his shirt. Seeing a bright shadow in front of him, he reached out to grapple with the thief. He hung on with all his strength, but the thief broke free, leaving his hands full of shining feathers.

He felt in his shirt. The apple was gone.

'Oh, well,' he said, 'at least I have some evidence.'

He tucked the feathers in his shirt and went to bed. Next morning, when the King asked for news of the thief, Petit Jean spread the feathers on the table.

'I couldn't hold him,' he said. 'But he left these behind in my hands.'

'A fine thing,' sneered his brothers, who were jealous of his success. 'To have the thief in your hands and let him go!'

'Hush!' said the King, staring at the bright feathers. 'I know this bird—it is the Golden Phoenix. No man can hold him against his will. Petit Jean, do you know in which direction he flew?'

'He left a fiery trail behind him, like a shooting star,' said Petit Jean. 'I saw him go over the top of the Glass Mountain.'

'Good,' said the King. 'We shall be able to follow his trail.'

And they all set off towards the Glass Mountain. Along the path from time to time they found a shining feather. But at the top of the Glass Mountain they stopped. They could see the shining feathers leading down into the Great Sultan's country. But they could not follow, for on this side the mountain fell away in a sheer cliff, a thousand feet straight down.

'We can go no farther,' said the King.

'Father, look,' said Petit Jean. 'I've found a trap-door.'

'A trap-door in a mountain?' scoffed his brothers. 'Ridiculous!'

'Please, Father, come and see,' repeated Petit Jean. 'Perhaps it leads down into the Great Sultan's country.'

The King came over to see the trap-door and decided it was worth looking into. All of them heaved together, and at last they managed to pull it open. Underneath they found a well going down into darkness.

'The sides are as smooth as ice,' said the elder princes. 'There is no way to climb down.'

'We need a good long rope,' said the King, 'and a stout basket on the end of it.'

These things were brought from the castle. To the end of the rope the princes tied a basket big enough for a man to sit in. On the King's advice they also attached a string to the basket, fastened at the other end to a bell.

'So if there is danger,' he explained, 'whoever is in the basket can signal us here at the top. Now, who is going down?'

The eldest prince turned white. 'Not I,' he said. 'I can't stand heights.'

The second prince turned green. 'Not I,' he said, 'I don't like the dark.'

Petit Jean laughed. 'Then it's my adventure,' he said. 'Wish me luck, Father.'

'Good luck, my boy,' said the King. 'And take with you this sword. Use it well, and it will keep you from harm. We shall keep watch here. When you come back and ring the bell, we will pull you up.'

Petit Jean said good-bye and climbed into the basket. Down, down, down he went, with the sword in one hand and the bell-rope in the other. For a long time he heard nothing and saw nothing. Then at last the basket stopped with a bump. He climbed out and gave two quick tugs on the bell-rope. Then he groped his way along a tunnel towards a faint light.

'Just as I thought,' he said. 'It leads into the Great Sultan's country.'

The light grew stronger, and the tunnel widened into a cavern. But here Petit Jean found his way barred. In the middle of the cavern stood a fierce beast with one long horn in the middle of its forehead. When it saw him it bellowed.

'I am the Unicorn of the Cave,' it said. 'You may not pass!'

'But I must pass,' said the prince. 'I am on my way to see the Sultan.'

'Then prepare for combat!' said the Unicorn.

And without another word it charged at him, the long sharp horn pointing straight at his heart. Petit Jean had no time to use his sword. At the last moment he dodged to one side, and the Unicorn thundered past. There was a terrific crash. The Unicorn had stuck fast in the wall of the cavern.

'Now may I pass?' asked Petit Jean.

'Yes, as far as I'm concerned,' grunted the Unicorn as it tried to work its horn free.

But Jean Petit could not pass. This time his way was barred by a great Lion, waving his tail menacingly.

'I am the Lion of the Cave,' he roared. 'Prepare for combat!'

And without another word he sprang straight at Petit Jean. The prince stood firm, and at the last moment swung his sword. *Snick!* He shaved the whiskers off the Lion's left cheek. With a fierce roar the Lion sprang again. Petit Jean swung his sword on the other side—*snick!*—and shaved the whiskers off the Lion's right cheek.

At this the Lion gave a deafening roar. He gathered himself for one more leap, and came down on Petit Jean with his paws out and his mouth open. This time the prince judged his moment very carefully. *Snick, snack!* And the Lion's head tumbled to the ground.

'Ouch!' said the Lion. Petit Jean was amazed to see him pick up his head with his front paws and set it on his neck again, as good as new.

'Now may I pass?' asked Petit Jean. 'Or must I do it again?'

'Oh, no,' said the Lion wearily. 'Once is enough for me.'

But Petit Jean still could not pass. The cavern was suddenly filled with a slithery hissing noise, and he found his way barred by a terrible beast with seven heads.

'I am the Serpent of the Cave,' hissed the beast. 'Prepare for combat!'

Petit Jean took a deep breath. This one looked very danger-ous indeed. But it did not spring at him. It just waited in his path. Wherever he tried to strike with his sword, he found a head snapping at him with fierce jaws and a forked tongue.

Then the young prince had a bright idea. He began running around the Serpent, striking with his sword; and the seven heads began to twist round each other trying to keep up with him. When the seven necks were twisted tight as a rope, he took a wide swing with his sword and—*snock!*—he cut off all seven heads at once. There was a roar of applause from the Unicorn and the Lion.

'Now may I pass?' asked Petit Jean again.

'You may pass,' sighed the Serpent, trying to find its seven heads and get them back on the right necks.

And so Petit Jean walked out into the realm of the Great Sultan. Just outside the cavern he found a glittering feather, so he knew he was still on the trail of the Golden Phoenix.

Before he had gone very far he was met by the Sultan him-

self riding on a white elephant. The Sultan had a long black moustache, and he stroked it as he looked down at his visitor.

'Who are you that have passed the Glass Mountain?' he asked. 'And what do you seek in my realm?'

'I am the son of your neighbour, the wise King,' replied Petit Jean. 'And I am looking for a bird that has been raiding our apple tree.'

3*

The sultan nodded thoughtfully. He invited Petit Jean to climb up on to the elephant behind him, and they rode back to the Sultan's palace. All along the road the prince kept his eyes open for the feathers that the Golden Phoenix had dropped in its flight.

When they reached the palace, the Sultan invited Petit Jean to dine with him in the garden. They were joined at the table by the Sultan's daughter, who was more beautiful than the moon and stars combined. Petit Jean could hardly take his eyes off her.

They sat down beneath a jasmine tree, and as they began the feast a bird sang above their heads, filling the evening air with beautiful music. Petit Jean caught a glimpse of gold among the leaves.

'May I ask what bird is singing, your highness?' he said.

The Sultan stroked his moustache. 'There are many birds in my realm,' he said. 'This one is probably a nightingale.'

Petit Jean thought it was probably something else; but he said no more about it. He complimented the Sultan on the food, which was delicious, and on his daughter, who looked more beautiful every moment.

When they had finished, the Sultan spoke to him again.

'It is the custom of this country,' he said, 'that every stranger passing through must play a game of hide-and-seek with me. To-morrow morning it will be your turn. If you should win, you shall have the hand of my daughter in marriage. How does that appeal to you?'

'It appeals to me more than anything else in the world,' said Petit Jean. 'But what if I should lose?'

The Sultan stroked his long black moustache and smiled. 'Ah,' he said. 'Then you will lose the dearest thing you own.'

'I see,' said Petit Jean. 'But I am a stranger here. How can I be expected to play hide-and-seek in a place I do not know?'

The Sultan nodded. 'This evening my daughter will show you round the garden. Take care to notice all the places where

I might hide, for to-morrow morning you must find me three times. And now I shall wish you good-night.'

When the Sultan had gone, the Princess began showing Petit Jean round the garden. But she noticed that he was not really paying attention.

'I think you do not wish to win my hand,' she said sadly, 'for you are not looking at anything I show you.'

'Dear Princess,' said Petit Jean, 'I would much rather look at you.'

The Princess could not help smiling. But suddenly she looked so sad that Petit Jean asked her what was the matter.

'I am thinking of what must happen to you to-morrow,' she said. 'I will tell you the truth: no matter how well you knew this garden, you would not be able to find my father. For he has the power to change his shape so that not even I can recognize him. So you see, nobody can win his game of hide-and-seek.'

'Then only luck can save me,' said Petit Jean cheerfully. 'Well, let us have no more sad talk. Tell me of yourself, Princess, and of the bird that sings over your banquet table.'

'The bird?' said the Princess. 'Oh, that is the Golden Phoenix. Whoever lives within the sound of its voice will never grow old.'

'A very useful bird,' said Petit Jean. 'And how do you make sure that it doesn't fly away?'

The Princess told him that the Phoenix did fly free during the night. But at sunrise he always came back to his golden cage. So whoever owned the cage could be sure of owning the Golden Phoenix.

They walked in the garden, talking of many things, until the moon rose. Then Petit Jean went to bed and slept soundly till morning.

Next day the Sultan was very cheerful, for he expected to win his game of hide-and-seek. He could hardly wait for Petit Jean to finish his breakfast.

'Now here are the rules of the game,' he said. 'I shall hide three times in the garden, and you must find me. And just to prove I am a fair man, I will offer you three prizes. If you find me once, you shall escape with your life. If you find me twice, you shall have your life and my daughter. If you find me three times, you shall have your life, my daughter, and whatever you choose as a dowry.'

'Agreed,' said Petit Jean.

The Sultan rushed off to hide, and Petit Jean invited the Princess to walk in the garden with him. She grew very pale and nervous, because he seemed to be making no effort to find her father.

At the Sultan's fish-pond they stopped and looked down. There were fishes of all colours and sizes swimming in it. Petit Jean looked at them closely and burst out laughing. One of the fishes had a long black moustache.

'Princess,' he said, 'I should like to borrow a net.'

'A net?' said the Princess. 'How can you think of fishing at a time like this?'

But she went and found him a net. Petit Jean leaned down and scooped out the fish with the moustache. There was a puff of white smoke, and the fish vanished. In its place was the Sultan, breathing hard.

'Humph!' growled the Sultan, climbing out of the net. 'And how did you happen to find me, young man?'

'Beginner's luck,' said Petit Jean. 'Well, have I earned my life?'

'Yes,' said the Sultan angrily. 'Do you want to stop there, or go on with the game?'

Petit Jean looked at the Princess. 'Oh,' he said, 'I shall go on.'

The Sultan rushed off to hide again. Petit Jean took the Princess's arm and they walked round the garden together. When she asked him where he would look this time, he shook his head.

'I don't know,' he said. 'I don't think your father will forget about his moustache again.'

They looked everywhere, but found nothing that turned out to be the Sultan. At last Petit Jean stopped beside a rose-bush and sighed.

'Well,' he said, 'if I am never to see you again, I would like to give you something to remember me by.'

And he leaned down to pluck the reddest rose on the bush. Pop! The rose disappeared in a puff of red smoke, and in its place stood the Sultan, red with anger.

'Oh!' exclaimed Petit Jean. 'I thought you were a rose.'

'You are too lucky for words,' snarled the Sultan. 'Well, you've won your life and my daughter. I suppose you want to stop there?'

'Oh, no,' said Petit Jean. 'That wouldn't be fair to you. I shall try my luck once more.'

And so the Sultan rushed off to hide for the last time. The Princess and Petit Jean went on walking in the garden, wondering where he might be. No matter where they tried, they could not find him.

At last Petit Jean stopped beneath a pear-tree.

'All this exercise is making me hungry,' he said. And reaching up, he plucked the ripest, roundest pear he could see.

Bang! There was a puff of black smoke, and in place of the pear stood the Sultan, black with fury.

'Oh,' said Petit Jean. 'I thought you were a pear.'

'You are too lucky to live!' roared the Sultan.

'But I have already won my life,' Petit Jean reminded him. 'And now I have won my choice of dowry.'

The Sultan grumbled, but finally asked what dowry Petit Jean would choose.

'A little thing which you'll hardly miss,' said Petit Jean. 'I choose the old gold cage which hangs in your daughter's chamber.'

The Sultan leaped into the air. 'The old gold cage!' he shouted. Then he pretended to be calm. 'Oh, you wouldn't want that old thing,' he said. 'Let me offer you three chests of treasure instead.'

'I couldn't possibly take your treasure,' said Petit Jean.
'The cage is quite enough.'

The Sultan turned purple with rage. But at last he agreed
that Petit Jean had won the cage fair and square. He even
promised to give them an escort as far as the Glass Mountain
next day.

Meanwhile there was a banquet to celebrate Petit Jean's
success, and above their heads the Golden Phoenix sang in the
jasmine tree. But all through the meal the Sultan kept pulling
his moustache and glancing angrily at Petit Jean. It was easy
to see that he was not at all happy.

The Princess noticed her father's mood, and as she had by
now fallen in love with Petit Jean, she felt nervous. When they
were alone together she told him her fears.

'I do not believe my father will keep his word,' she said.
'He is so angry at losing the Golden Phoenix that he will try
to kill you while you sleep.'

'Then we had better leave during the night,' said Petit
Jean.

The Princess agreed. 'Bring two horses from the stable, and
muffle their hooves,' she said. 'Meanwhile I will fetch my
travelling cloak and the golden cage.'

Petit Jean tiptoed to the stable and chose two horses. He
tied pieces of blanket around their hooves and led them back
to the kitchen door. There he met the Princess, wearing her
cloak and carrying the cage.

'My father is suspicious,' she said. 'But as long as he hears
voices talking he will not stir from his room.'

She put two beans into a frying-pan on the stove. As soon as
they felt the heat the beans began to croak. One of them said
'Nevertheless' in a high voice; the other said 'Notwithstanding' in a deep voice. When they were both croaking they
sounded just like a man and woman together.

Petit Jean and the Princess mounted their horses and rode
softly away, carrying the golden cage, while upstairs the
Sultan listened to the conversation in the kitchen. He had a

sleepless night, for the two beans went on saying 'Nevertheless—notwithstanding' until morning. And by the time he found out what had happened, Petit Jean and the Princess had reached the Glass Mountain.

The Unicorn, the Lion, and the Serpent were there in the cavern, but they did not bar the way. Petit Jean placed his Princess in the basket and pulled on the bell-rope. His father and brothers were waiting at the top, and when they heard the bell they pulled the basket up the well.

They were astonished to see the Princess. The two princes would have stopped and gazed at her, but she told them to let down the basket again before it was too late. Presently they pulled up Petit Jean with the golden cage in his arms.

'Welcome home, my boy,' said the King. 'And welcome to your lady, too. But where is the bird you set off to find? This cage is empty.'

Petit Jean pointed to the Great Sultan's country, and they saw a dazzling radiance moving towards them through the sky, with a beating of golden wings: for it was near daybreak, and the Phoenix was looking for his cage. And after him on the road below came the Sultan himself, riding his white elephant and shaking his fist at the sky.

The three princes rolled a big stone over the trap-door so that the Sultan could never follow them. Then, with the Golden Phoenix safe in his cage, they set off homewards.

Petit Jean and his Princess were married, and the King gave them his crown and kingdom as he had promised. And with the Golden Phoenix singing every night in the tree where the silver apple of wisdom grew, they lived wisely and happily ever afterwards.

From *The Golden Phoenix* by Marius Barbeau retold by Michael Hornyansky (Oxford University Press, Toronto; Henry Z. Walck, Inc., New York)

(See Note, page 154)

The Hare, the Lions,
the Monkey and Hare's Spotted Blanket

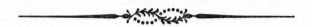

NOW KALULU the Hare was making for himself a blanket from the bark of a certain tree. But the bark of the tree was very hard. For many days Hare worked at the blanket, but he could not make it soft.

Then Hare became tired. And Hare said, 'Some one must make this blanket for me.' And Hare thought of Lion, who is very strong and can make a good blanket.

So Hare went to Lion's house, and Lion was in the house. But Hare hid in a bush near by to the house.

And presently Lion and his wife went out to hunt. And when Lion and his wife went out, Hare went in; and Hare found Lion's child in the house.

And Hare said, 'Where is Lion, your father? I have a job for him.'

And Lion's child said, 'My father and my mother have gone out to hunt for food.'

Then Hare put down the piece of bark and said, 'Here is work for your father to do. He must make a soft blanket with the bark for a certain man; your father must make it very soft and very quickly.'

And Lion's child said, 'I will tell him.'

But Lion's child did not know who Hare was.

And Hare went away to his house.

And after a while, Lion and his wife returned from hunting. And Lion saw Hare's piece of bark in the house, and he said, 'What is this?'

And Lion's child said, 'A certain man came and he said, "Here is work for your father to do. He must make a soft blanket with the bark; your father must make it very soft and very quickly." '

And Lion said, 'But what is the name of this certain man?'

And Lion's child said, 'I do not know him, father.'

So Lion took Hare's piece of bark and made of it a very soft blanket.

And next day Hare said, 'I must see how that fellow, Lion, is getting on with my blanket.'

So Hare went to Lion's house and hid in a bush near by to the house.

And when Lion and his wife went out of the house to hunt, Hare went in; and Hare found Lion's child in the house.

And Hare said, 'Where is Lion, your father, and has he finished making my blanket for me?'

And Lion's child said, 'My father and my mother have gone out to hunt for food, but my father has finished making the blanket for you.'

And Hare saw that the blanket that Lion had made was a good one. Then Hare said, 'You must tell your father that my blanket is all right, but he must now put some spots on it so that the blanket may be a pretty one.'

And Lion's child said, 'I will tell him.'

Then Hare went away to his home.

And after a while, Lion and his wife returned from hunting.

And Lion's child said, 'A certain man has been here and he said, "My blanket is all right, but your father must now put some spots on it so that the blanket may be a pretty one." '

And Lion said, 'Who, then, is this certain man who says I must work for him?'

And Lion's child said, 'I do not know him, father.'

So Lion took Hare's blanket and he put some spots on it. He put the spots of leopard and of cheetah and of bushbuck, so that the blanket was a very pretty one.

And next day Hare said, 'I must see how that fellow, Lion, is getting on with my blanket.'

So Hare went to Lion's house and hid in a bush near by to the house.

And Lion and his wife and their child went down to the river to drink. And when Lion and his wife and their child had gone out of the house, Hare went in. And Hare found his blanket there. And Lion had made the blanket pretty with many spots.

So Hare took the blanket and went away to his house.

And when Lion and his wife and their child came back from drinking at the river, they saw that someone had taken away the blanket. Then Lion became very angry and said, 'Who then is this certain man who thinks that I must work for him and receive no payment?'

Then Lion made a plan to catch that one who had made him do some work but had given him no payment for that work.

And Lion prepared a big dinner, and he asked all the animals to his dinner. And Hare also was asked to the dinner.

And on the day of the big dinner, Hare took his spotted blanket which Lion had made, and he sat down by the side of the path along which all must pass in going to the dinner at Lion's house.

And many animals passed by on their way to the big dinner. And some of the animals had on good clothes, but the clothes of some were not so good. And presently came Monkey.

And Hare said, 'Good day to you, Monkey.'

And Monkey said, 'Good day to you, Hare, my friend.'

'Where are you going, Monkey?'

'I go to the big dinner at Lion's house, Hare.'

'I, too, am going there, Monkey. We will go together.'

And Hare and Monkey went on together.

And on the way, Hare said, 'How is it, Monkey, that you have no nice blanket for the dinner?'

And Monkey said, 'I cannot make a blanket, Hare.'

Then Hare said, 'It is not a good thing for a big man like you, Monkey, to go to Lion's dinner without a nice blanket.'

And Monkey said, 'What can I do, Hare?'

And Hare said, 'As you are my friend, Monkey, I shall lend you my spotted blanket. But you must not say "Hare lent me this blanket."'

So Hare gave Monkey his spotted blanket, and Hare and Monkey went on and came together to Lion's house.

And when Lion saw Monkey he said, 'There is the certain man who said I must work for him; but he gave me no payment for my work. Am I his slave?'

And Lion who was very angry ran after Monkey. But Monkey ran away from Lion for fear of him. And Monkey climbed up to the top of a very high tree and so escaped from Lion.

But as he ran, Monkey had dropped Hare's spotted blanket.

And Hare said, 'Lion, I shall take this spotted blanket and keep it for myself as I have no blanket.'

And Lion said, 'Hare, you may keep it.'

So Hare went to the big dinner with his spotted blanket.

But Monkey, who was much afraid of Lion, remained in the big tree.

From *African Aesop* by Frank Worthington (Wm. Collins, Glasgow)

(See Note, page 155)

The Dancing Princesses

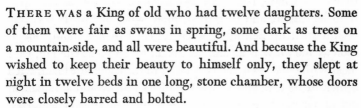

THERE WAS a King of old who had twelve daughters. Some of them were fair as swans in spring, some dark as trees on a mountain-side, and all were beautiful. And because the King wished to keep their beauty to himself only, they slept at night in twelve beds in one long, stone chamber, whose doors were closely barred and bolted.

Yet, in spite of this, as soon as the year came round to May again, and the stars and cold of winter were gone and the world was merry, at morning and every morning the soles of the twelve princesses' slippers were found to be worn through to the very welts. It was as if they must have been dancing in them all the night long.

News of this being brought to the King, he marvelled. Unless they had wings, how could they have flown out of the Palace? There was neither crevice nor cranny in the heavy doors. He spied. He set watch. It made no difference. Brand-new though the princesses' gold and silver slippers were overnight, they were worn out at morning. He was in rage and despair.

At last this King made a decree. He decreed that anyone who, by waking and watching, by wisdom or magic, should reveal this strange secret, and where and how and when the twelve princesses' slippers went of nights to get so worn, he should have the hand in marriage of whichever one of the princesses he chose, and should be made the heir to the throne. As for anyone foolish enough to be so bold as to attempt such a task and fail in it, he should be whipped out of the kingdom, and maybe lose his ears into the bargain. But, such was the beauty of these princesses, many a high-born stranger lost, not only his heart, but his ears also; and the King grew ever more moody and morose.

Now beyond the walls of the royal house where lived the twelve princesses was a forest; and one summer's evening an old soldier who was travelling home from the wars met there, on his way, a beldame with a pig. This old beldame had brought her pig to the forest to feed on the beech-mast and truffles, but now, try as she might, she could not prevail upon it to be caught and to return home with her to its sty. She would steal up behind it with its cord in her hand, but as soon as she drew near and all but in touch of it, the pig, that meanwhile had been busily rooting in the cool loose loam, with a flick of its ears and a twinkle of its tail, would scamper off out of her reach. It was almost as if its little sharp glass-green eyes could see through the pink shutters of its ears.

The old soldier watched the pig (and the red sunlight was glinting in the young green leaves of the beeches), and at last he said: 'If I may make so bold, Grannie, I know a little secret about pigs. And if, as I take it, you want to catch *that* particular pig, it's yours and welcome.'

The beldame, who had fingers like birds' claws and eyes black as sloes, thanked the old soldier. Fetching out a scrap of some secret root from the bottom of his knapsack, he first slowly turned his back on the pig, then stooped down and, with the bit of root between his teeth, stared earnestly at the pig from between his legs.

Presently, either by reason of the savour of the root or drawn by curiosity, the pig edged closer and closer to the old soldier, until at last it actually came nosing and sidling in underneath him, as if under a bridge. Then in a trice the old soldier snatched him up by the ear and tail, and slipped the noose of the cord fast. The pig squealed like forty demons, but more as if in fun than in real rage.

'There we are, Grannie,' said the old soldier, giving the old beldame her pig, 'and here's a scrap of the root, too. There's no pig all the world over, white, black, or piebald, but after he gets one sniff of it comes for more. *That* I'll warrant you, and I'm sure you're very welcome.'

The beldame, with her pig now safely at the rope's end and
the scrap of root between her fingers, thanked the old soldier
and asked him of his journey and whither he was going; and
it was just as if, with its snout uplifted, its ears drawn
forward, the nimble young pig was also listening for his
answer.

The old soldier told her he was returning from the wars.
'But as for where *to*, Grannie, or what for, I hardly know.
For wife or children have I none, and most of my old friends
must have long ago forgotten me. Not that I'm meaning to say,
Grannie,' says the soldier, 'that *that* much matters, me being
come so far, and no turning back. Still, there's just *one* thing
I'd like to find out before I go, and that is where the twelve
young daughters of the mad old King yonder dance of nights.
If I knew that, Grannie, they say I might some day sit on a
throne.' With that he burst out laughing, at which the pig,
with a twist of its jaws (as though recalling the sweet savour
of the root), flung up its three-cornered head and laughed too.

The beldame, eyeing the old soldier closely, said that what
he had asked was not a hard or dangerous matter, if only he
would promise to do exactly what she told him. The old
soldier found *that* easy enough.

'Well,' said the beldame, 'when you come to the Palace,
you'll be set to watch, and you'll be tempted to sleep. Vow a
vow, then, to taste not even a crumb of the sweet cake or sip
so much as a sip of the wine the princesses will bring to you
before they go to bed. Wake and watch; then follow where
they lead; and here is a cloak which, come fair or foul, will
make you invisible.' At this the beldame took a cloak finer
than spider silk from out of a small bag or pouch she wore,
and gave it him.

'That hide me!' said the soldier. 'Old coat, brass buttons,
and all?'

'Ay,' said the beldame, and thanked him again for his
help; and the pig coughed, and so they parted.

When she was out of sight the old soldier had another look

at the magic cloak, and thought over what the beldame had told him. Being by nature bold and brave, and having nothing better to do, he went off at once to the King.

The King looked at the old soldier, listened to what he said, and then with a grim smile half-hidden under his beard, bade him follow him to a little stone closet hard by the long chamber where the princesses slept. 'Watch here,' he said, 'and if you can discover this secret, then the reward I have decreed shall be yours. If not . . .' He glanced up under his brows at the brave old soldier (who had no more fear in his heart than he had money in his pocket), but did not finish his sentence.

A little before nightfall, the old soldier sat himself down on a bench in the stone closet, and by the light of a stub of candle began to mend his shoe.

By-and-by the eldest of the princesses knocked softly on his door, smiled on him and brought him a cup of wine and a dish of sweet cakes. He thanked her. But as soon as she was gone he dribbled out the wine drip by drip into a hole between the flagstones, and made crumbs of the cakes for the mice. Then he lay down and pretended to be asleep. He snored and snored, but even while he snored he was busy with his cobbler's awl boring a little hole for a peephole between the stone of the wall where he lay and the princesses' room. At midnight all was still.

But hardly had the little owl of midnight called, *Ahoo! ahoo! ahoo!* when the old soldier, hearing a gentle stirring in the next room, peeped through the tiny hole he had bored in the wall. His eyes dazzled; a wondrous sight was to be seen. For the princesses in the filmy silver of the moon were now dressing and attiring themselves in clothes that seemed not of this world, but from some strange otherwhere, which they none the less took out of their own coffers and wardrobes. They seemed to be as happy as larks in the morning, or like swallows chittering before they fly, laughing and whispering together while they put on these bright garments and made

ready. Only one of them, the youngest, had withdrawn herself a little apart and delayed to join them, and now kept
silent. Seeing this, her sisters made merry at her, and asked
her what ailed her.

'The others,' she said, 'whom our father set to watch us
were young and foolish. But that old soldier has wandered all
over the world and has seen many things, and it seems to
me he is crafty and wise. That, sisters, is why I say,
Beware!'

Still they only laughed at her. 'Crafty and wise, forsooth!'
said they. 'Listen to his snoring! He has eaten of our sweet
cakes and drunken the spiced wine, and now he will sleep
sound till morning.' At this the old soldier, peeping through
his little bore-hole in the stones, smiled to himself, and went
on snoring.

When they were all ready to be gone, the eldest of the
princesses clapped her hands. At this signal, and as if by magic,
in the middle of the floor one wide flagstone wheeled softly
upon its neighbour, disclosing an opening there, and beneath
it a narrow winding flight of steps. One by one, according to
age, the princesses followed the eldest down this secret stair-
case, and the old soldier knew there was no time to be
lost.

He flung the old beldame's cloak over his shoulders, and (as
she had foretold) instantly of himself there showed not even
so much as a shadow. Then, having noiselessly unbarred the
door into the princesses' bedroom, he followed the youngest of
them down the stone steps.

It was dark beneath the flagstones, and the old soldier trod
clumsily in his heavy shoes. And as he groped down he
stumbled, and trod on the hem of the youngest princess's
dress.

'Alas, sisters, a hand is clutching at me!' she called out to
her sisters.

'A hand!' mocked the eldest. 'You must have caught your
sleeve on a nail!'

On and down they went, and out of a narrow corridor at last emerged and came full into the open air, and following a faint track in the green turf, reached at last a wood where the trees (their bark, branches, twigs and leaves) were all of silver and softly shimmering in a gentle light that seemed to be neither of sun nor moon nor stars. Anon they came to a second wood, and here the trees shone softly too, but these were of gold. Anon they came to a third wood, and here the trees were in fruit, and the fruits upon them were precious stones—green, blue, and amber, and burning orange.

When the princesses had all passed through this third wood, they broke out upon a hillside, and, looking down from out the leaf-fringed trees, the old soldier saw the calm waters of a lake beyond yellow sands, and drawn up on its strand twelve swan-shaped boats. And there, standing as if in wait beside them, were twelve young men that looked to be princes. Noble and handsome young men they were.

The princesses, having hastened down to the strand, greeted these young men one and all, and at once embarked into the twelve swan-shaped boats, the old soldier smuggling himself as gingerly as he could into the boat of the youngest. Then the princes rowed away softly across the water to an island that was in the midst of the lake, where was a palace, its windows shining like crystal in the wan light that bathed sky and water.

Only the last of the boats lagged far behind the others, for the old soldier sitting there invisible on the thwart, though little else but bones and sinews, weighed as heavy as a sack of stones in the boat. At last the youngest of the princes leaned on his oars to recover his breath. 'What,' he sighed, 'can be amiss with this boat to-night? It never rowed so heavily.'

The youngest of the princesses looked askance at him with fear in her eyes, for the boat was atilt with the weight of the old soldier and not trimmed true. Whereupon she turned her small head and looked towards that part of the boat where sat the old soldier, for there it dipped deepest in the water. In so doing, she gazed straight into his eyes, yet perceived nothing but the green water beyond. He smiled at her, and—though she knew not why—she was comforted. 'Maybe,' she said, turning to the prince again and answering what he had said—'maybe you are wearied because of the heat of the evening.' And he rowed on.

When they were come to the island and into the palace there, the old soldier could hardly believe his eyes, it was a scene so fair and strange and unearthly. All the long night through, to music of harp and tambour and pipe, the princesses danced with the princes. Danced, too, the fountains at play, with an endless singing of birds, trees with flowers blossoming, and no-one seemed to weary. But as soon as the scarlet shafts of morning showed beyond these skies, they returned at once to the boats, and the princesses were soon back safely under the King's roof again, and so fast asleep in their beds that they looked as if they had never stirred or even sighed in them the whole night long. They might be lovely images of stone.

But the old soldier slept like a hare—with one eye open. When he awoke, which was soon, he began to think over all that he had seen and heard. The longer he pondered on it, the more he was filled with astonishment. Every now and then, as if to make sure of the land of the living, he peeped with his eye through the hole in the wall, for he was almost of a mind to believe that his journey of the night before—the enchanted woods, the lake, the palace and the music—was nothing more than the make-believe of a dream.

So, being a man of caution, he determined to say nothing at all of what had passed this first night, but to watch again a second night. When dark drew on, he once more dribbled out the spiced wine in the crannies of the stones and crumbled the sweet cakes into morsels for the mice, himself eating nothing but a crust or two of rye-bread and a rind of cheese that he had in his haversack.

All happened as before. Midnight came. The princesses rose

up out of their beds, gay and brisk as fish leaping at evening out of their haunts, and soon had made ready and were gone to their trysting-place at the lake-side. All was as before.

The old soldier—to make sure even surer—watched for the third night. But this night, as he followed the princesses, first through the wood where the leaves were of silver, and next where they resembled fine gold, and last where the fruits on the boughs were all of precious stones, he broke off in each a twig. As he did so the third time, the tree faintly sighed, and the youngest princess heard the tree sigh. Her fears of the first night, far from being lulled and at rest, had only grown sharper. She stayed a moment in the wood, looking back, and cried, ' Sisters! Sisters! We are being watched. We are being followed. I heard this tree sigh, and it was in warning.' But they only laughed at her.

' Sigh, forsooth!' they said. ' So, too, would you, sister, if you were clad in leaves as trees are, and a little wind went through your branches.'

Hearing this, in hope to reassure her, the old soldier softly wafted the three twigs he carried in the air at a little distance from the youngest's face. Sweet was the scent of them, and she smiled. That night, too, for further proof, the old soldier stole one of the gold drinking-cups in the princes' palace and hid it away with the twigs in his haversack. Then for the last time he watched the dancing, and listened to the night birds' music and the noise of the fountains. But being tired, he sat down and yawned, for he had no great wish to be young again, and was happy in being himself.

Indeed, as he looked in at the princesses, fast, fast asleep that third early morning, their dreamless faces lying waxen and placid amid the braids of their long hair upon their pillows, he even pitied them.

That very day he asked to be taken before the King, and when he was come into his presence entreated of him a favour.

'Say on!' said the King. The old soldier then besought the King to promise that if he told the secret thing he had dis, covered he would forgive the princesses all that had gone before.

'I'd rather,' he said, 'be whipped three times round your Majesty's kingdom than open my mouth else.'

The King promised. Then the old soldier brought out from his haversack the three twigs of the trees—the silver and the gold and the begemmed—and the gold cup from the banqueting hall ; and he told the King all that had befallen him.

On first hearing of this, the King fell into a rage at the thought of how his daughters had deceived him. But he remembered his promise and was pacified. He remembered, too, the decree he had made, and sent word that his daughters should be bidden into his presence. When they were come, the dark and the fair together, he frowned on them, then turned to the old soldier : 'Now choose which of these deceivers you will have for wife, for such was my decree.'

The old soldier, looking at them each in turn, and smiling at the youngest, waved his great hand and said : 'My liege, there is this to be said : Never lived any man high or low that *deserved* a wife as gentle and fair as one of these. But in the place of enchantment I have told of, there were twelve young princes. Well,spoken and soldierly young men they were ; and if it was choosing sons I was, such are the sons I would choose. As for myself, now—if I may be so bold, and if it would be any ease to your Majesty's mind—it being a promise, in a manner of speaking—there's one thing, me having roved the world over all my life, I'm mortal anxious to *know* . . .' and here he paused.

'Say on,' said the King.

'Why,' replied the old soldier, 'what sort of thing it feels like to sit, even though but for the mite of a moment, on a throne.'

On hearing this, the King grasped his beard and laughed heartily. 'Easily done,' he cried. 'The task is to stay there.'

With his own hand he led the old soldier to the throne, placed his usual crown upon his head, the royal sceptre in his hand, and with a gesture presented him to all assembled there. There sat the old soldier, with his war-worn face, great bony hands and lean shanks, smiling under the jewelled crown at the company. A merry scene it was.

Then the King earnestly asked the old soldier if he had anything in mind for the future, whereby he might show him

his favour. Almost as if by magic, it seemed, the memory of the beldame in the forest came back into the old soldier's head, and he said: 'Well, truth's truth, your Majesty, and if there *was* such a thing in my mind, it was pigs.'

'Pigs!' cried the King. 'So be it, and so be it, and so be it! Pigs you shall have in plenty,' said he. 'And by the walls of Jerusalem, of all the animals on God's earth there's none better—fresh, smoked, or salted.'

'Ay, sir,' said the old soldier, 'and even better still with
their plump-chapped noddles still on their shoulders and the
breath of life in their bodies!'

Then the King sent for his Lord Steward and bade that
seven changes of raiment should be prepared for the old
soldier, and two mules saddled and bridled, and a fat purse of
money put in his hand. Besides these, the King commanded
that out of the countless multitude of the royal pigs should be

chosen threescore of the comeliest, liveliest and best, with two
lads for their charge.

And when towards sundown a day or two after, the old
soldier set out from the Royal House into the forest with his
laden mules, his pigs and his pig-lads, besides the gifts that
had been bestowed on him by the twelve noble young princes
and princesses, he was a glad man indeed. But most he prized
a worn-out gold and silver slipper which he had asked of the

youngest princess for a keepsake. This he kept in his knapsack with his magic scrap of root and other such treasures, as
if for a charm.

From *Tales Told Again* by Walter de la Mare (Faber & Faber, London;
Alfred A. Knopf, New York)

(See Note, page 155)

The Goat Well

A MAN named Woharia was once travelling across the plateau
when he came to an abandoned house. He was tired and
hungry, so he rested in the house and ate some of his bread.
When he was about to leave he heard the baa-ing of a goat.
He looked in all directions, but he saw nothing except the dry
brown landscape. He heard the goat again, and finally he went
to the old well and looked down into it. There, standing on the
dry bottom, was the animal, which had somehow fallen in
while searching for water to drink.

'What luck!' Woharia said. He climbed down and tied a
rope round the goat, and then he came up and began to
pull her out of the well.

Just at this moment a Cunama trader, with three camels
loaded with sacks of grain, approached him. He greeted
Woharia and asked if he might have water there for his
thirsty camels.

'Naturally, if there were water here you would be welcome
to it,' Woharia said. 'But unfortunately this is a goat
well.'

'What is a goat well?' the Cunama asked.

'What do you think? It's a well that produces goats,'
Woharia said, and he pulled on his rope again until he got
the goat to the top.

'This is really extraordinary!' the Cunama said. 'I've
never before heard of a goat well!'

'Why, I suppose you're right,' Woharia said. 'They aren't
very common.'

'How does it work?' the Cunama trader asked.

'Oh, it's simple enough,' Woharia said. 'Every night you
throw a pair of goat's horns into the well, and in the

morning you find a goat. Then all you have to do is to draw
her out.'

'Unbelievable!' the Cunama said. 'Man, how I'd like to
own such a well!'

'So would everyone else,' Woharia said, untying the goat
and letting her run loose. 'But few people can afford to buy
such an unusual thing.'

'Well, I'll tell you,' the Cunama said, thinking very hard.
'I'm not a rich man, but I'll pay you six bags of durra grain
for it.'

Woharia laughed.

'That wouldn't pay for many goats,' he said.

'I'll give you twelve bags of durra, all that my camels are carrying!' the Cunama said anxiously.

Woharia smiled and shook his head.

'Seven goats a week,' he said as though he were talking to

himself. 'Thirty goats a month. Three hundred and sixty-five goats a year. . . .'

But the Cunama had set his heart on owning the well.

'Look at my young sleek camels! I have just bought them in Keren! Where will you ever find better camels than these? I'll give you my twelve bags of grain and my three camels also. I'd give you more, but I own nothing else in the whole world, I swear it to you!'

Woharia thought silently for a moment.

'Since you want it so much, I'll sell it to you,' he said finally.

The Cunama leaped down from his camel and embraced Woharia.

'For this goodness may you live long!' he said. 'May Allah bring you many good things to give you joy!'

'Ah,' said Woharia, looking at the camels, 'he has already done so.'

He took the three camels loaded with grain, his goat, and his few other possessions, and prepared to leave.

'Before you go, tell me your name?' the Cunama asked.

'People call me Where-I-shall-Dance,' Woharia replied. And then he went away to the south, leaving the Cunama with the well.

The Cunama was very impatient to begin getting goats from the well. When evening came, he dropped two goat's horns into it and lay down in the house to sleep. The next morning, when it was barely light, he rushed out again to draw up his first goat, but when he peered into the well, he saw nothing except the old horns he had thrown in.

'There must be some mistake!' he said to himself.

That evening he threw down two more horns, and again in the morning he rushed out to get his first goat, but once more he saw only the old goat's horns there. This time he was very worried. He scoured the country to find old goat's horns, and he threw armful after armful into the well. And all night long he sat by the well, shouting into it:

'Goats, are you there? Goats, are you there?'

But nothing at all happened. When morning came at last the Cunama was angry and unhappy. He realized that he had been duped by his own anxiousness to get the well. There was nothing left to do but to go out and find the man who had taken his camels and his precious grain.

The trader travelled southward, as Woharia had done. At last, when night had fallen, he came to a village. When he arrived in the village square, where many people were gathered, he went up to them and asked:

'Do you know Where-I-Shall-Dance?'

'Why, it doesn't matter, dance anywhere you like,' the people answered. 'Dance right here if you wish!' And they began to sing and make music for him.

'No, no, you don't understand,' he said. 'What I want to know is, do you know Where-I-Shall-Dance?'

'Yes, dance here!' they said again.

The Cunama was very angry because he thought that the people were making fun of him, so he went out of the village and continued his journey southward, stopping only to sleep at the edge of the road.

The next day, he came to another village, and he went to the market place and said in a loud voice:

'Does anybody know Where-I-Shall-Dance?'

The people gathered around him instantly and shouted:

'Dance here! Dance here!'

They clapped their hands and a drummer came and beat his drum, and everyone waited for the Cunama to dance.

He turned and fled from the village, believing that the people were ridiculing him. Again, he came to a village, and again he asked:

'Do you know Where-I-Shall-Dance?'

And once more the people began clapping their hands and answered:

'Yes, dance here!'

The same thing happened in every village the man entered. He began to feel very hopeless, and sometimes thought he might even be losing his mind. He began to be afraid to ask his question. Finally, one day, he came to the village of the chief of the district. When he asked his question here and the people gave him the usual answer, the news was carried to the chief, who immediately sent for him.

'Now, what sort of nonsense is this?' the chief asked. 'You

ask the people where you should dance and then you refuse to dance.'

The unhappy man told how he had bought the dry well in exchange for his three young camels and his grain. The chief listened sympathetically. He remembered that a man named Woharia had recently settled in a nearby village, and that he had come with three camels and twelve bags of grain.

'Sit down and rest,' the chief said. 'I will handle the matter now.'

He sent a messenger to Woharia, and when the messenger found him he said, as he had been instructed:

'There is a man waiting to see you at the house of the chief. His name is What-I-Shall-Do. The chief wishes you to come at once.'

Woharia went immediately to the house of the chief, and the servants let him in.

'What can I do for you?' the chief asked.

'Why, do you know What-I-Shall-Do?' Woharia asked.

'Yes, I know what you shall do,' the chief said. 'You shall give back the Cunama trader his three camels and his twelve bags of grain.'

Woharia was crestfallen and ashamed. He gave the Cunama back the camels and the grain. The Cunama took them and went out. As he passed the market place the people shouted:

'Dance here! Dance here!'

And the trader was so happy that this time he danced in the market place.

From *The Fire on the Mountain* by Harold Courlander and Wolf Leslau (Holt, Rinehart & Winston, New York)

(See Note, page 156)

Mister Rabbit

Response group points to parts of the body mentioned.

CALL   Mister Rabbit, Mister Rabbit,
Your ears are mighty long.
RESPONSE   *Yes, my friend,*
They're put on wrong!

Mister Rabbit, Mister Rabbit,
Your coat's mighty grey.
Yes, my friend,
'Twas made that way!

Mister Rabbit, Mister Rabbit,
Your feet are mighty red.
Yes, my friend,
I'm almost dead!

Mister Rabbit, Mister Rabbit,
Your tail's mighty white.
Yes, my friend,
And I'm getting
Out of sight!

From *Did you Feed my Cow?* by Margaret Taylor (Thomas Y. Crowell, New York)

(See Note, page 153)

The Snooks Family

ONE NIGHT Mr and Mrs Snooks were going to bed as usual. It so happened that Mrs Snooks got into bed first, and she said to her husband, 'Please, Mr Snooks, would you blow the candle out?' And Mr Snooks replied, 'Certainly, Mrs Snooks.' Whereupon he picked up the candlestick and began to blow, but unfortunately he could only blow by putting his under lip over his upper lip, which meant that his breath went up to the ceiling instead of blowing out the candle flame.

And he puffed and he puffed and he puffed, but he could not blow it out.

So Mrs Snooks said, 'I will do it, my dear,' and she got out of bed and took the candlestick from her husband and began to blow. But unfortunately she could only blow by putting her upper lip over her under lip, so that all her breath went down on to the floor. And she puffed and she puffed, but she could not blow the candle out.

So Mrs Snooks called their son John. John put on his sky-blue dressing-gown and slipped his feet into his primrose-coloured slippers and came down into his parents' bedroom.

'John, dear,' said Mrs Snooks, 'will you please blow out the candle for us?' And John said, 'Certainly, Mummy.'

But unfortunately John could only blow out of the right corner of his mouth, so that all his breath hit the wall of the room instead of the candle.

And he puffed and he puffed and he puffed, but he could not blow out the candle.

So they all called for his sister, little Ann. And little Ann put on her scarlet dressing-gown and slipped on her pink slippers and came down to her parents' bedroom.

'Ann, dear,' said Mr Snooks, 'will you please blow the

candle out for us?' And Ann said, 'Certainly, Daddy.'

But unfortunately Ann could only blow out of the left side of her mouth, so that all her breath hit the wall instead of the candle.

And she puffed and she puffed and she puffed, but she could not blow out the candle.

4*

It was just then that they heard in the street below a heavy, steady tread coming along the pavement. Mr Snooks threw open the window and they all craned their heads out. They saw a policeman coming slowly towards the house.

'Oh, Mr Policeman,' said Mrs Snooks, 'will you come up and blow out our candle? We do so want to go to bed.'

'Certainly, Madam,' replied the policeman, and he entered and climbed the stairs,—blump, blump, blump. He came into the bedroom where Mr Snooks, Mrs Snooks, John Snooks and little Ann Snooks were all standing round the candle which they could *not* blow out.

The policeman then picked up the candlestick in a very dignified manner and, putting his mouth into the usual shape for blowing, puffed out the candle at the first puff. Just like this—PUFF!

Then the Snooks family all said, 'Thank you, Mr Policeman.' And the policeman said, 'Don't mention it,' and turned to go down the stairs again.

'Just a moment, Policeman,' said Mr Snooks. 'You mustn't go down the stairs in the dark. You might fall.' And taking a box of matches, he LIT THE CANDLE AGAIN!

Mr Snooks went down the stairs with the policeman and saw him out of the door. His footsteps went blump, blump, blump along the quiet street.

John Snooks and little Ann Snooks went back to bed. Mr and Mrs Snooks got into bed again. There was silence for a moment.

'Mr Snooks,' said Mrs Snooks, 'would you blow out the candle?'

Mr Snooks got out of bed. 'Certainly, Mrs Snooks,' he said. . . .

And so on *ad infinitum.*

From *Tales from Ebony* by Harcourt Williams (Putnam, London)

(See Note, page 157)

Jean Labadie's Big Black Dog

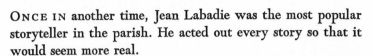

ONCE IN another time, Jean Labadie was the most popular storyteller in the parish. He acted out every story so that it would seem more real.

When he told about the great falls of Niagara, he made a booming noise deep in his throat and whirled his fists around each other. Then each listener could plainly hear the falls and see the white water churning and splashing as if it were about to pour down on his own head. But Jean Labadie had to stop telling his stories about the *loup-garou*, the demon who takes the shape of a terrible animal and pounces upon those foolish people who go out alone at night. Every time the storyteller dropped down on all fours, rolled his eyes, snorted, and clawed at the floor, his listeners ran away from him in terror.

It was only on the long winter evenings that Jean had time to tell these tales. All the rest of the year, he worked hard with his cows and his pigs and his chickens.

One day Jean Labadie noticed that his flock of chickens was getting smaller and smaller. He began to suspect that his neighbour, André Drouillard, was stealing them. Yet he never could catch André in the act.

For three nights running, Jean took his gun down from the wall and slept in the henhouse with his chickens. But the only thing that happened was that his hens were disturbed by having their feeder roost with them, and they stopped laying well. So Jean sighed and put his gun back and climbed into his own bed again.

One afternoon when Jean went to help his neighbour mow the weeds around his barn, he found a bunch of grey chicken feathers near the fence. Now he was sure that André was taking his chickens, for all of his neighbour's chickens were scrawny white things.

He did not know how to broach the matter to André without making an enemy of him. And when one lives in the country and needs help with many tasks, it is a great mistake to make an enemy of a close neighbour. Jean studied the matter as his scythe went swish, swish through the tall weeds. At last he thought of a way out.

'Have you seen my big black dog, André?' he asked his neighbour.

'What big black dog?' asked André. 'I didn't know you had a dog.'

'I just got him from the Indians,' said Jean. 'Someone has been stealing my chickens so I got myself a dog to protect them. He is a very fierce dog, bigger than a wolf and twice as wild.'

Jean took one hand off the scythe and pointed to the ridge behind the barn.

'There he goes now,' he cried, 'with his big red tongue hanging out of his mouth. See him!'

André looked but could see nothing.

'Surely you must see him. He runs along so fast. He lifts one paw this way and another paw that way.'

As Jean said this, he dropped the scythe and lifted first one hand in its black glove and then the other.

André looked at the black gloves going up and down like the paws of a big black dog. Then he looked toward the ridge. He grew excited.

'Yes, yes,' he cried, 'I do see him now. He is running along the fence. He lifts one paw this way and another paw that way, just like you say.'

Jean was pleased that he was such a good actor he could make André see a dog that didn't exist at all.

'Now that you have seen him,' he said, 'you will know him if you should meet. Give him a wide path and don't do anything that will make him suspicious. He is a very fierce watchdog.'

André promised to stay a safe distance from the big black dog.

Jean Labadie was proud of himself over the success of his trick. No more chickens disappeared. It seemed that his problem was solved.

Then one day André greeted him with, 'I saw your big black dog in the road to-day. He was running along lifting one paw this way and another paw that way. I got out of his way, you can bet my life!'

Jean Labadie was pleased and annoyed at the same time. Pleased that André believed so completely in the big black dog that he could actually see him. He was also annoyed because the big black dog had been running down the road when he should have been on the farm.

Another day André leaned over the fence.

'Good day, Jean Labadie,' he said. 'I saw your big black dog on the other side of the village. He was jumping over fences and bushes. Isn't it a bad thing for him to wander so far away? Someone might take him for the *loup-garou*.'

Jean Labadie was disgusted with his neighbour's good imagination.

'André,' he asked, 'how can my dog be on the other side of the village when he is right here at home? See him walking through the yard, lifting one paw this way and another paw that way?'

André looked in Jean's yard with surprise.

'And so he is,' he agreed. 'My faith, what a one he is! He must run like lightning to get home so fast. Perhaps you should chain him up. Someone will surely mistake such a fast dog for the *loup-garou*.'

Jean shrugged hopelessly.

'All right,' he said, 'perhaps you are right. I will chain him near the henhouse.'

'They will be very happy to hear that in the village,' said André. 'Everyone is afraid of him. I have told them all about him, how big and fierce he is, how his long red tongue hangs out of his mouth and how he lifts one paw this way and another paw that way.'

Jean was angry.

'I would thank you to leave my dog alone, André Drouillard,' he said stiffly.

'Oh, ho, and that I do,' retorted André. 'But to-day on the road he growled and snapped at me. I would not be here to tell the story if I hadn't taken to a tall maple tree.'

Jean Labadie pressed his lips together.

'Then I will chain him up this very moment.' He gave a long low whistle. 'Come, fellow! Here, fellow!'

André took to his heels.

Of course, this should have ended the matter, and Jean Labadie thought that it had. But one day when he went to the village to buy some nails for his roof, he ran into Madame Villeneuve in a great how-does-it-make of excitement.

'Jean Labadie,' she cried to him, 'you should be ashamed of yourself, letting that fierce dog run loose in the village.'

'But my dog is chained up in the yard at home,' said Jean.

'So André Drouillard told me,' said Madame, 'but he has broken loose. He is running along lifting one paw this way and another paw that way, with the broken chain dragging in the dust. He growled at me and bared his fangs. It's a lucky thing his chain caught on a bush or I would not be talking to you now.'

Jean sighed.

'Perhaps I should get rid of my big black dog,' he said. 'To-morrow I will take him back to the Indians.'

So next day Jean hitched his horse to the cart and waited until he saw André Drouillard at work in his garden. Then he whistled loudly toward the yard, made a great show of helping his dog climb up between the wheels and drove past André's house with one arm curved out in a bow, as if it were around the dog's neck.

'*Au revoir*, André!' he called. Then he looked at the empty half of the seat. 'Bark good-bye to André Drouillard, fellow, for you are leaving here forever.'

Jean drove out to the Indian village and spent the day with his friends, eating and talking. It seemed a bad waste of time when there was so much to be done on the farm, but on the other hand, it was worth idling all day in order to end the big black dog matter.

Dusk was falling as he rounded the curve near his home. He saw the shadowy figure of André Drouillard waiting for him near his gate. A feeling of foreboding came over Jean.

'What is it?' he asked his neighbour. 'Do you have some bad news for me?'

'It's about your big black dog,' said André. 'He has come back home. Indeed he beat you by an hour. It was that long ago I saw him running down the road to your house with his big red tongue hanging out of his mouth and lifting one paw this way and another paw that way.'

Jean was filled with rage. For a twist of tobacco, he would have struck André with his horsewhip.

'André Drouillard,' he shouted, 'you are a liar! I just left the big black dog with the Indians. They have tied him up.'

André sneered.

'A liar am I? We shall see who is the liar. Wait until the others see your big black dog running around again.'

So Jean might as well have accused André of being a chicken thief in the first place, for now they were enemies anyway. And he certainly might as well have stayed home and fixed his roof.

Things turned out as his neighbour had hinted. Madame Villeneuve saw the big black dog running behind her house. Henri Dupuis saw him running around the corner of the store. Delphine Langlois even saw him running through the grave-yard among the tombstones. And always as he ran along, he lifted one paw this way and another paw that way.

There came that day when Jean Labadie left his neighbour chopping wood all by himself, because they were no longer friends, and drove into the village to have his black mare shod. While he was sitting in front of the blacksmith shop, André Drouillard came galloping up at a great speed. He could scarcely hold the reins, for one hand was cut and bleeding.

A crowd quickly gathered.
'What is wrong, André Drouillard?' they asked.
'Have you cut yourself?'
'Where is Dr Brisson? Someone fetch Dr Brisson.'

André Drouillard pointed his bleeding hand at Jean Labadie.

'His big black dog bit me,' he accused. 'Without warning, he jumped the fence as soon as Jean drove away and sank his teeth into my hand.'

There was a gasp of horror from every throat. Jean Labadie reddened. He walked over to André and stared at the wound.

'It looks like an axe cut to me,' he said.

Then everyone grew angry at Jean Labadie and his big black dog. They threatened to drive them both out of the parish.

'My friends,' said Jean wearily, 'I think it is time for this matter to be ended. The truth of it is that I have no big black dog. I never had a big black dog. It was all a joke.'

'Aha!' cried André. 'Now he is trying to crawl out of the blame. He says he has no big black dog. Yet I have seen it with my own eyes, running around and lifting one paw this way and another paw that way.'

'I have seen it, too,' cried Madame Villeneuve. 'It ran up and growled at me.'

'And I.'

'And I.'

Jean Labadie bowed his head.

'All right, my friends,' he said. 'There is nothing more I can do about it. I guess that big black dog will eat me out of house and home for the rest of my life.'

'You mean you won't make things right about this hand?' demanded André Drouillard.

'What do you want me to do?' asked Jean.

'I will be laid up for a week at least,' said André Drouillard, 'and right at harvest time. Then, too, there may be a scar. But for two of your plumpest pullets, I am willing to overlook the matter and be friends again.'

'That is fair,' cried Henri Dupuis.

'It is just,' cried the blacksmith.

'A generous proposal,' agreed everyone.

'And now we will return to my farm,' said Jean Labadie, 'and I will give André two of my pullets. But all of you must come. I want witnesses.'

A crowd trooped down the road to watch the transaction. It was almost as large as the one that had attended Tante Odette's skunk party.

After Jean had given his neighbour two of his best pullets, he commanded the crowd, 'Wait!'

He went into the house. When he returned, he was carry- ing his gun.

'I want witnesses,' explained Jean, 'because I am going to shoot my big black dog. I want everyone to see this happen.'

The crowd murmured and surged. Jean gave a long low whistle toward the henhouse.

'Here comes my big black dog,' he pointed. 'You can see how he runs to me with his big red tongue hanging out and lifting one paw this way and another paw that way.'

Everyone saw the big black dog.

Jean Labadie lifted his gun to his shoulder, pointed it at nothing and pulled the trigger. There was a deafening roar and the gun kicked Jean to the ground. He arose and brushed off his blouse. Madame Villeneuve screamed and Delphine Langlois fainted.

'There,' said Jean, brushing away a tear, 'it is done. That is the end of my big black dog. Isn't that true?'

And everyone agreed that the dog was gone for good.

From *The Talking Cat* by Natalie Savage Carlson (Harper & Row, New York)

(See Note, page 157)

The Princess on the Glass Hill

ONCE UPON a time there lived a farmer who had one field which was a very long way from his house. The grass grew well there and made fine hay.

But on the morning after Midsummer Eve, the farmer found that the hay in this field had been cropped as short as if a great flock of sheep had feasted there all night long. So on the next Midsummer Eve, the farmer said that one of his three sons must sleep up there in the barn and catch the thief.

The eldest son was pleased to go and he swore that the grass would not be touched while *he* was there. So as the sun set, he went and lay down to watch.

In the middle of the night there was a crash of thunder and the whole barn shook with an earthquake. The eldest son didn't wait for any more—he ran home as if the devil were after him and, in the morning, all the grass had been eaten to the roots.

Well, the farmer wasn't very pleased as you can guess, and next Midsummer Eve he sent his second son to watch. At midnight the same thing happened—the thunder crashed and an earthquake shook the barn from side to side. The second son didn't wait—he ran home as if the devil were after him, and, in the morning, the grass had been eaten to the roots once more.

The third year, the youngest son, who was called Boots, took his turn. His elder brothers said that if they couldn't stay the night, neither could he. All he was fit for was to sit among the ashes, but Boots said nothing and went to the field and sat down to wait.

Oh my! In the middle of the night there was a clap of

thunder so loud that the boy's ears nearly split. Then the barn shook as if it had a fever.

'Well, if that's all,' said Boots, 'I'm not afraid.'

Another earthquake came and the barn nearly fell to pieces. When all was quiet again, Boots said cheerfully:

'That's not so bad, either. I can stand it.'

A third earthquake gave the barn such a jolt that Boots was tossed up to the ceiling. When he came down again and had dusted the hay off his clothes, he sat down and began to eat his bread and cheese.

'Well, that's nothing to make a fuss about,' he said.

Now all was still and silent and as Boots listened, he heard a sound like a horse cropping the grass. He crept to the door and, looking through a crack, he saw a fine horse feeding in the moonlight. On the ground was a saddle and a bridle made of gleaming brass and a fine suit of armour as well.

'So you're the thief who eats my father's hay!' cried Boots. 'I'll soon put paid to that.'

He took the steel out of his tinder box—everyone knows that that is magic—and threw it over the horse's head. At once the horse stood still as if it were made of stone. Boots took the armour and rode the horse away to a secret place he knew of.

In the morning the two elder brothers said scornfully:

'I don't suppose you ever went near the field.'

'That I did and stayed there all night,' said Boots. 'A fine sleep I had too!'

The brothers went to the field and there, sure enough, was the grass as thick and ready for cutting as on the day before.

Next Midsummer Eve the same thing happened. Boots held on through the earthquake and, when all was still, there was another horse cropping the grass. Once again Boots found a suit of armour and this time it was of shining silver.

'So you're the thief who eats my father's hay!' cried Boots. 'I'll soon put paid to that.'

He threw the steel from his tinder box over the horse's head and rode it away to his secret place.

The third year the same thing happened. The earthquakes were so bad that Boots danced up and down, hitting the roof each time. Then there was silence and through the door Boots saw a still more wonderful horse cropping the grass. On the ground a suit of golden armour worth a king's ransom glowed like the sun. Boots rode the third horse to his secret place.

You can imagine that Boots' success in guarding the grass didn't make him any more popular with his brothers. They were as spiteful and cruel as they could be, but Boots said nothing as he sat among the ashes.

Now close to the King's palace there was a high hill made all of glass. It was as slippery as ice and as steep as a house. The King had a beautiful daughter and he said that she should sit on the top of the hill with three golden apples in her lap. The man who could ride up the hill and take the apples should marry the Princess and have half the kingdom as well.

The Princess was so beautiful that, hard as the task was, every prince in the world wanted to try his luck.

The day of the trial came and a wonderful assembly of princes in shining armour gathered at the Glass Hill. Everybody came to look at them and so Boots' brothers went along too. Boots asked if he could go with them but they said that he was too dirty, for he had to clean shoes and sift cinders all the day long.

'Very well,' said Boots. 'I'll go by myself.'

So there was the Glass Hill and all the princes had a try to ride up it. As fast as they rode up a few inches, they slipped down again. Not one of them could get up it even a little way and their horses were so weary at the end of the day that their heads hung down and they couldn't lift a hoof from the ground.

Suddenly there was a clatter of hooves in the distance and

up rode a strange knight. He was dressed in a suit of brass armour that gleamed in the setting sun. He put his horse at the hill and rode a third of the way up it as easily as anything. The Princess liked the look of him so much that she threw

him a golden apple. He picked it up in a flash and rode away like the wind.

When Boots' brothers came home that night, they had a fine tale to tell of the mysterious knight in brass armour.

'I should have liked to have seen him, that I should!' said Boots, but the brothers only laughed at him scornfully.

Next day the brothers set off again but they would not take Boots with them, beg as he might.

'Very well,' said Boots. 'I can go by myself.'

Once more the princes tried to ride up the Glass Hill. They

had all had the shoes of their horses sharpened so that they could climb better. But it was no use—the horses grew so weary that they could not lift a hoof.

Suddenly there was a clatter of hooves in the distance and a knight rode up on a fine horse. He was wearing a suit of silver armour. Oh, how the silver shone in the light of the setting sun! He rode up the hill two-thirds of the way quite easily and the Princess hoped that he would get to the top. But he turned and rode down again, so she had to throw him the second golden apple. He picked it up in a flash and rode away like the wind.

The two brothers told Boots about the knight in silver armour that night. 'How he could ride!' they said and Boots exclaimed:

'I should have liked to have been there, I should.'

On the third day, the princes were soon tired and so were their horses. They waited to see if the knight in silver would come again, but in his place there rode up a knight on a magnificent horse with golden trappings. The knight was wearing a suit of golden armour so bright that it dazzled everyone. He rode up the Glass Hill so fast the the Princess scarcely had time to wish he would get to the top, when he snatched the third golden apple from her lap and galloped down the other side of the hill and disappeared.

The brothers went home and told Boots about the knight in golden armour. 'Oh, what a magnificent sight he was!' they said and Boots exclaimed: 'Oh, how I wish I had been there!'

Next day the King asked all the princes to pass before him so that the one who had the golden apples might make himself known. Not one of the princes could produce the apples!

'Someone has them, that is sure!' said the King. 'Every man and boy in the kingdom must come to the palace until we find the one who has the golden apples.'

One by one, men and boys filed past the King until there were only two left—Boots' brothers.

'Isn't there anyone else to come?' asked the King.

'Well, we have a brother,' they said, 'but he sits in the ashes all day long, so it can't be him.'

The King insisted that Boots should come and along he came in his dirty sooty rags.

'Have *you* got the golden apples?' asked the King and everybody shouted with laughter at the idea.

Boots put his hand in his pocket and there were the three golden apples in his hand for everyone to see! 'Here they are,' he said proudly, and he threw off his dirty clothes and stood there in his magnificent golden armour.

'You shall have my daughter and half my kingdom and that gladly,' said the King. 'You have won them fairly.' The Princess was not sorry either to have Boots as a husband for she had liked him from the first.

And they all feasted right royally at the wedding and lived happily ever after as far as I know.

Traditional, adapted by Eileen Colwell.

(See Note, page 158)

Zini and the Witches

THERE WAS once a young Brave, called Zini, who married a woman from a far-away tribe. She had a very beautiful voice, and every night she would sing Zini to sleep, but always the songs were in a language he did not understand.

One night he said to her, 'What are those songs that you sing to me, my wife?'

'Sleepy songs,' she answered, 'the ancient songs of my people.'

'I wish I might know what the words mean,' said Zini. And she answered, 'This is what they mean:

'Go to sleep, my darling, my love,
Go to sleep, my darling.
Sleep soundly, sleep soundly, my darling, my love,
Go to sleep, my darling.
Sleep till dawn wakes you, my darling, my love,
Go to sleep, my darling!'

'Oh, is that what they mean?' said Zini.

'Yes,' said she. 'What else should they mean?'

But Zini was puzzled. It seemed to him that the songs didn't sound quite like that. He was so puzzled that he dreamed he was caught in a monstrous spider's web, and then he woke up.

'Sing me to sleep again, my wife,' he said.

But there was no answer. His wife had gone.

In the morning she was back again by his side. He thought he would ask her where she had been; and then he thought he wouldn't. Instead, he went to the Medicine Man, and told him.

The Medicine Man shook his head. 'I fear she has taken the wrong road,' he said.

By which he meant she wasn't good but bad.

He told Zini to look all round the house when his wife was out, especially in places where it was dark.

When Zini got home, his wife was just coming out with a brightly painted jar on her head. She was going to the spring for water. The spring was some way off. Zini thought now was his chance to look round the house, and to save time he decided to look in the dark places first. He looked in one dark place and saw nothing. And he looked in another dark place and saw nothing. And then he lifted a curtain to look in a third dark place, and he saw—it isn't easy to say what he saw. There were bodies and bones, and all sorts of horrors. So then Zini knew his wife was a witch.

He went off to the Medicine Man again, and this time he was crying.

'You must keep awake to-night,' said the Medicine Man, and he gave Zini a little red seed. 'Put this on your tongue and you won't go to sleep, let her sing as long as she will. But you must pretend to sleep, and then watch what happens, and come to me again.'

So that night Zini put the little red seed on his tongue before he went to bed. His wife began to sing to him, and he yawned and sighed and closed his eyes, but he was wide, wide awake. His wife was a little bit suspicious—perhaps he wasn't breathing quite right for a sleeping man. At any rate she sang much longer than usual.

By and by a big black cat came creeping in and stood at the top of the steps.

'We are all waiting for you,' whispered the cat. 'Why don't you come?'

'You must wait for me a little while,' said the wife. 'The man is stirring in his sleep.'

Then Zini lay very, very still. He breathed gently and evenly—he even snored a little.

By and by a big grey owl flew down through the smoke

hole. 'You must hurry,' whispered the owl, 'the Chief is getting angry.'

The wife looked at Zini. 'He is asleep now,' she said, and she tiptoed away and climbed the ladder out of the house.

Zini got up and followed her, keeping in the shadows. It

was a bright moonlight night, and though he kept at a distance he could see her moving from the shadows into the light and back into the shadows again. He followed her till they came to a black mountain. At the bottom of the mountain was a big, dark cave. The mouth of the cave was dripping with

water, and the moon shone on the water and turned it into
a white rainbow. The wife passed under the white rainbow,
and as she did so she became a pink cat.

Zini stood under the rainbow and peered into the cave.

There was a fire blazing in the middle of the cave, and

witches were flying in through the walls. As they alighted on
the floor they turned into animals and birds, vultures and
wolves and lynxes and owls and cats. Behind the fire the
Witch Chief sat on a throne. The throne was a huge bat,
and the Chief sat between its wings. The bat had its head

down, and the Chief used its head as a footstool. The bat didn't look at all comfortable, but when it tried to move, the Chief kicked it, and then it was still again.

'You are very late,' said the Witch Chief to the pink cat; and he gave her four scratches with his long nails, two scratches on her face, and two on her chest.

'I can't help it,' said the pink cat angrily, 'my husband is getting to suspect me. He asked me what my songs meant, but I fooled him.'

And she told the Chief what she had said to Zini.

'And what do the words of the song really mean?' asked the Witch Chief.

'What do they mean?' said the pink cat. 'This is what they mean:

> 'Go to sleep, you horrible man,
> Go to sleep, you horror.
> Sleep soundly, sleep soundly, you horrible man,
> Go to sleep, you horror.
> Sleep till I wake you, you horrible man,
> Go to sleep, you horror.'

'Ha! Ha! Ha!' laughed the Witch Chief. And 'Ha! Ha! Ha!' laughed all the vultures and wolves and lynxes and owls and cats.

Then they looked up and saw Zini peeping in under the white rainbow.

Zini tried to run away, but they rushed at him and dragged him into the cave. They tied his hands behind his back and stood him before the Chief.

'You deserve to die for this,' said the Chief. 'But I will spare your life on one condition. Bring me the hearts of your mother and sister and you shall live. Not only shall you live, but you shall become one of us. We will turn you into a mighty witch, and you shall help your wife to work evil.' Then he ordered the creatures to free Zini's arms, and told him to go home. 'To-morrow night I shall expect you again, with your offering of hearts,' he said. 'If you do not come, I shall see to it that your wife skins you alive.'

Zini didn't go home, he went to the Medicine Man and told him what had happened.

'This is terrible,' said the Medicine Man. 'I scarcely know what we can do.' He thought for a long time, and then he said, 'You will have to go back to the cave to-morrow night, that is certain. But you cannot cut out the hearts of your mother and sister. You must kill two sheep and carry their hearts to the Witch Chief. We may be able to deceive him, but I doubt it.' The Medicine Man shook his head, and shook his head. 'I fear trouble will come of it,' he said.

Then he gave Zini a little red shell, and told him to hide it in the folds of his shirt. 'It will at least protect your life, if it will do no more,' he said.

So Zini hid the little red shell in the folds of his shirt, and he went home and killed two sheep. His wife didn't come home all that day, and he was glad rather than sorry. When night came, he wrapped the two sheeps' hearts in a napkin made of cat-tail reeds and carried them to the cave.

The Witch Chief was there, sitting behind the fire on his bat-throne, and the pink cat was there, and all the other creatures. They were having a feast, taking all sorts of un-pleasant things out of a big oven, and swallowing everything down smoking hot.

'I have brought you the hearts,' said Zini to the Chief. He was as frightened as could be, but he was trying not to show it.

The Chief told the pink cat to put the hearts in the oven. By and by they began to sizzle.

'Ba-a-a-a!' they said.

'Was your mother a sheep, and was your sister a sheep?' said the Witch Chief.

'Of course not,' answered Zini. 'But they had a sheep for their totem.' He had to say something, and that was the first thing he thought of.

The Chief pretended to be satisfied with his explanation, and he told Zini to go home and lie down to sleep.

It seemed to Zini that he did go home, but that was only the Witch Chief's magic. When Zini woke in the morning, he found himself lying on a ledge of rock. The ledge was half-way up a great cliff. Below the ledge, the cliff went down for a thousand feet, as steep and straight as a house wall; and above the ledge, the cliff rose up another thousand feet, equally steep and straight, and there wasn't a crack or a crevice anywhere in the cliff that a man could climb up or down by.

The ledge was only just wide enough to take Zini's body, and he couldn't move backwards or forwards or sideways. He was lying on his back, and the sun was beating down on his head. He lay there all day without moving, and when night came it was bitterly cold, and his shirt froze to the ledge. And when morning came, the sun beat down on him again, and he felt he was being roasted alive. He didn't die, because the little red shell in the fold of his shirt kept him alive, but he suffered from heat and cold and hunger and thirst and giddiness, and he almost felt that it would be better if he could die.

When the sun was high on the third day, a baby squirrel came *hoppity-skip* along the ledge. He saw Zini's moccasins sticking up and climbed on to one of them. Then he sat down and wrinkled his nose and looked along Zini's body as far as his face. Zini's eyes were closed, he didn't even seem to be breathing.

'Nana! Nana!' called Baby Squirrel, 'I've found a dead man on our ledge!'

Then Mother Squirrel came along, *hoppity-skip, hoppity-skip*; and she climbed on to Zini's other moccasin and looked along his body to his face. Zini opened his eyes and stared at the sky, and then he shut his eyes again.

'He's not dead,' said Mother Squirrel, 'but I think he's starving.' She took an acorn cup out of her cheek. 'Here, son,' she said to Baby Squirrel, 'fill this with corn meal and water.'

Baby Squirrel took the acorn cup, jumped down off Zini's moccasin, and went off, *hoppity-skip, hoppity-skip*. In less than no time he was back again, with the cup filled with wet corn meal.

Mother Squirrel took the cup from him, and ran *hoppity-skip, hoppity-skip*, all the way along Zini's body till she came to his face.

'Eat!' she said.

Zini raised his neck, very stiffly, and looked down at the acorn cup. Then he gave a very small smile and shook his head. It was kind of Mother Squirrel, but what good would a tiny lick of corn meal like that be to him?

'Eat! Eat!' said Mother Squirrel, holding the acorn cup to his lips. 'You must eat to get strong. It may look a little, but it's more than enough.'

So then, to please her, Zini ate the wet corn meal. He ate and ate, and still the acorn cup was full. He ate until he could eat no more, and then he gave a big smile and said, 'Thank you!'

'Feeling better?' said Mother Squirrel.

'Much, much better,' said Zini.

Hoppity-skip, hoppity-skip, Mother Squirrel went off and came back with a cedar branch. This she laid over Zini's head to protect him from the sun. And when night came she was back again, *hoppity-skip*, with a bark-fibre blanket, and this she laid over him to protect him from the cold.

Three times a day Baby Squirrel brought him the acorn cup full of wet corn meal, and between whiles he sat on Zini's moccasin and told him stories to pass away the time. And when he was tired of telling stories, he danced. He did a War Dance, and a Buffalo Hunt Dance, and the Sun Dance, and the Dance to Scare Away False Faces That Look At You Out of The Trees. He danced every dance he knew.

'But you must watch me,' he said to Zini. 'I can't dance properly if you don't.'

5

So Zini lifted up his neck and watched Baby Squirrel strutting around on his moccasin, and stamping.

'Ha! Ha! Yahi-yahi! Yeh!' shouted Baby Squirrel.

'Ha! Ha! Yahi-yahi! *Yoh!*' answered Zini, and that pleased Baby Squirrel mightily.

Zini even managed to clap his hands now and then. He was feeling ever so much stronger.

Mother Squirrel was busy doing something else. She went to her store-place and fetched a pine cone. Then she came and stood at Zini's feet, and dropped the pine cone over the cliff. The pine cone fell down, down, a thousand feet down. Mother Squirrel peeped over the edge and watched it falling.

'Grow, grow, pine cone grow! Grow, grow, grow!' she said.

In the morning, after Baby Squirrel had brought him his breakfast, Zini felt so much stronger that he was able to sit up. He raised himself very, very carefully, so as not to topple sideways, and then he too peered over the edge. Down, down, a thousand feet down, he saw a great plain with green grass and a river, and close against the cliff a little pine tree was growing. When he looked again in the evening, the little pine was a tall tree, and when he looked again next morning, its topmost branches reached half-way up the cliff. Every time he looked at it, it had grown taller; by the fourth morning its topmost branches were on a level with the ledge, and by the fourth evening it towered, strong and mighty, high above his head, and a great branch of it lay against the ledge close to Zini's hand.

Hoppity-skip! Mother Squirrel was dancing on the branch. 'Now, friend Zini,' she said, 'it's time to go home. Take hold of the branch and follow me.'

Hoppity-skip! Baby Squirrel jumped on to Zini's shoulder; Zini grasped the branch with both hands and swung himself off the ledge. *Hoppity-skip!* Mother Squirrel was dancing on the branch just below. Zini swung himself on to that branch, and so they went, down, down, a thousand feet down, till they stood side by side on the plain.

'Now, friend Zini, it's time to say good-bye,' said Mother Squirrel. 'Follow the river, and you'll soon get home.'

Zini thanked her and thanked her. 'Pooh!' said Mother Squirrel, 'it would be a poor world if we couldn't do *that* much for each other!' Then she gave him some pine tree seeds and some pinyon nuts.

'When you get home,' she said, 'give your wife the pine seeds, but you yourself must eat the pinyon nuts. Now remember—pine seeds for her, pinyon nuts for you. It's very important.'

Zini said he would remember, and thanked her again. Then they said good-bye to each other. Mother Squirrel and Baby Squirrel climbed back up the tree, and Zini went along by the river and found himself back in his own village.

His wife was very surprised to see him. 'Why,' said she, 'I thought you were dead! You've been away four years, and now I've married another man.'

'Poor fellow!' thought Zini. But he was glad to know that she wasn't *his* wife any more. He went in and talked pleasantly to the new husband. The poor man looked scared; he grasped Zini by the hand and said he was very glad he had come back.

'Oh, I've brought you some pine seeds,' said Zini to his wife and she took them and ate them, and Zini and the new husband shared the pinyon nuts between them. After that, the new husband made up a bed on the floor for Zini, and the wife sang them both to sleep. Early in the morning, Zini and the new husband went out hunting together, and the wife busied herself about the house.

'I shan't expect you back till sunset,' she said to the men.

Zini wondered if they would ever come back; but he said nothing, and the new husband said nothing. Each of them shot a fine fat buck; and towards sunset, not knowing what else to do, they returned to the village.

But when they drew near their house they stopped and stared. The wicked wife had vanished, and in her place, pushing up through the roof, and growing high above it, was a great pine tree. Its dark branches were thrust out through the sides of the house, and they were waving about like arms, as if they were trying to catch hold of something. But there was nothing to catch hold of, and from the pine tree came a mighty sighing, like waves on a far-off shore. Sometimes the sighing grew louder, and sometimes it grew softer, but it never stopped.

And it will never stop as long as that pine lives.

By and by the pine grew so big that it cracked the walls round it, and the house fell down in pieces. But Zini and the new husband built themselves another house, where they lived together like good friends. They went hunting together, and they went fishing together; and after a bit they married two sisters, who were both good women, and they all four lived happily for the rest of their lives.

From *Red Indian Folk and Fairy Tales* by Ruth Manning-Sanders (Oxford University Press, London; Roy, New York)

(See Note, page 159)

Where Arthur Sleeps

THERE WAS once a young man in west Wales who was the seventh son of a seventh son. All such, it is said, are born to great destinies, for with their forty-nine parts of man there is blended one part of Bendith y Mamau (Blessing of the Mothers, or fairies). It happened one day that he quarrelled with his father and left home to seek his fortune in England. As he walked through Wales he met a rich farmer who engaged him to take a herd of cattle to London. 'For to my eyes,' said the farmer, 'you look a likely lad, and a lucky one too. With a dog at your heels and a staff in your hand you would be a prince among drovers. Now here is a dog, but where in the world is a staff?'

'Leave that to me,' said our Welshman, and stepping aside to a rocky mound he cut himself the finest hazel stick he could find. It had to be fine, for as teeth to a dog so his staff to a drover. It was tall as his shoulder and mottled like a trout, and so hard of grain that when the sticks of his fellow-drovers were ragged as straws it showed neither split nor splinter.

He passed through England without losing a beast and disposed of his herd in London. A little later he was standing on London Bridge, wondering what to do next, when a stranger stopped alongside him and asked him from whence he came.

'From my own country,' he replied; for a Welshman does well to be cautious in England.

'And what is your name?' asked the stranger.

'The one my father gave me.'

'And where did you cut your stick, friend?'

'I cut it from a tree.'

'I approve your closeness,' said the stranger. 'Now what would you say if I told you that from that stick in your hand I can make you gold and silver?'

'I should say that you are a wise man.'

'With Capital Letters at that,' said the stranger, and he went on to explain that this hazel stick had grown over a place where a vast treasure lay hidden. 'If only you can remember where you cut it, and lead me there, that treasure shall be yours.'

'I may well do that,' said the Welshman, 'for why am I here save to seek my fortune?'

Without more ado they set off together for Wales and at last reached Craig-y-Dinas [The Fortress Rock], where he showed the Wise Man (for such he was) the exact spot where he had cut his stick. It had sprung from the root of a large old hazel, and the knife-mark was still to be seen, as yellow as gold and broad as a broad-bean. With bill and mattock they dug this up and found underneath a big flat stone; and when they lifted the stone they saw a passage and a gleam at the far end of it.

'You first,' said the Wise Man; for an Englishman does well to be cautious in Wales; and they crept carefully down the passage towards the gleam. Hanging from the passage roof was a bronze bell the size of a bee-hive, with a clanger as long as your arm, and the Wise Man begged the Welshman on no account to touch it, for if he did disaster would surely follow. Soon they reached the main cave, where they were amazed by the extent of it, and still more by what they saw there. For it was filled with warriors in bright armour, all asleep on the floor. There was an outer ring of a thousand men, and an inner ring of a hundred, their heads to the wall and their feet to the centre, each with sword, shield, battle-axe and spear; and outermost of all lay their horses, unbitted and unblinkered, with their trappings before their noses. The reason why they could see this so clearly was because of the extreme brilliance of the weapons and the glitter of the armour, the helmets glowing like suns and the hooves of the horses effulgent as autumn's moon. And in the middle of all lay a King and Emperor at rest, as they knew by the splendour of his array and the jewelled crown beneath his hand and the awe and majesty of his person.

Then the Welshman noticed that the cavern also contained two tall heaps of gold and silver. Gaping with greed he started towards them, but the Wise Man motioned to him to wait a moment first.

'Help yourself,' he warned him, 'from one heap or the other, but on no account from both.'

The Welshman now loaded himself with gold till he could not carry another coin. To his surprise the Wise Man took nothing.

'I have not grown wise,' he said, 'by coveting gold and silver.'

This sounded more wind than wisdom to the Welshman, but he said nothing as they started for the mouth of the cave. Again the Wise Man cautioned him about touching the bell. 'It might well prove fatal to us if one or more of the warriors

should awake and lift his head and ask, "Is it day?" Should
that happen there is only one thing to do. You must instantly
answer: "No, sleep on!" and we must hope that he will
lower his head again to rest, by which means we may escape.'

And so it happened. For the Welshman was now so bulging
with gold that he could not squeeze past the bell without
touching it. At once a sonorous clangour of bronze bewrangled
the passage, and a warrior lifted his head.

'Is it day?' he asked.

'No,' replied the Welshman, 'sleep on.'

At these prompt words the warrior lowered his head and
slept, and not without many a backward glance the two
companions reached the light of day and replaced the stone
and the hazel tree. The Wise Man next took his leave of the

Welshman, but gave him this counsel first. 'Use that wealth well,' he told him, 'and it will suffice you for the rest of your life. But if, as I suspect, you need to come for more, you may return and help yourself from the silver heap. Try not to touch the bell, but if you do and a warrior awakes, he will ask: "Are the Cymry in danger?" You must then answer "Not yet, sleep on!" But I should on no account advise you to return a third time.'

'Who are these warriors?' asked the Welshman. 'And who is their sleeping king?'

'The king is Arthur, and those that surround him are the men of the Island of the Mighty. They sleep with their steeds and their arms because a day will come when land and sky shall cower at the clamour of a host, and the bell will tremble and ring, and then those warriors will ride out with Arthur at their head, and drive our foes headlong into the sea, and there shall be justice and peace among men as long as the world endures.'

'That may be so, indeed,' said the Welshman, waving farewell. 'Meantime I have my gold.'

But the time soon came when the gold was all spent. A second time he entered the cave, and a second time took too great a load, only this time of silver. A second time his elbow touched the bell. Three warriors raised their heads. 'Are the Cymry in danger?' The voice of one was light as a bird's, the voice of another was dark as a bull's, and the voice of the third so menacing that he could hardly gasp out an answer. 'Not yet,' he said, 'sleep on!' Slowly, with sighs and mutter-ings, they lowered their heads, and their horses snorted and clashed their hooves before silence filled the cave once more.

For a long time after this escape he told himself that he would on no account return to the cave a third time. But in a year or two his silver went the way of the gold, and almost despite himself there he was, standing by the hazel with a mattock in his hand. A third time he entered the cave and a third time took too great a load, this time of silver and gold as well. A third time his elbow touched the bell. As it boomed, all those warriors sprang to their feet, and the proud stallions with them, and what with the booming of the bell, the jangling of the armour, and the shrill neighing of the horses, never in the world's history was there more uproar in an enclosed place than that. Then Arthur's voice arose over the din, silencing them, and Cei and the one-handed Bedwyr, Owein, Trystan, and Gwalchmei, moved through the host and brought the horses to a stand.

'The time is not yet,' said Arthur. He pointed to the Welshman, trembling with his gold and silver in the passage. 'Would you march out for him?'

At these words, Cei caught the intruder up by the feet and would have lashed him against the wall, but Arthur forbade it and said to put him outside, and so Cei did, flinging him like a wet rabbit-skin from the passage and closing the stone behind him. So there he was, without a penny to scratch with, blue as a plum with fright and bruises, flat on his back in the eye of the sun.

It was a long time before he could be brought to tell his story, and still longer before he grew well. One day, however, he returned, and some friends with him, to Craig-y-Dinas.

'Where is the hazel tree?' they asked, for it was not to be seen. 'And where is the stone?' they asked, for they could not find it. When he persisted in his story they jeered at him, and because he might not be silenced they beat him, and so it came about that for shame and wrath he left the country-side for ever. And from that day to this no one, though he were seven times over the seventh son of a seventh son, has beheld Arthur sleeping with his host, nor till the day of Britain's greatest danger shall any so behold him. So with the hope that that day is a long way off, we reach the end of our story.

From *Welsh Legends and Folk Tales* by Gwyn Jones (Oxford University Press, London; Henry Z. Walck, Inc., New York)

(See Note, page 160)

Old Ponto

Dramatise actions suggested by the lines.

CALL

Old Ponto is dead
And laid in his grave.

RESPONSE

Laid in his grave.
Laid in his grave.
Old Ponto is dead
And laid in his grave.
Sob! Sob! Sob!

There grew a large apple tree
Over his grave.
Over his grave.
Over his grave.
There grew a large apple tree
Over his grave.
Sob! Sob! Sob!

The apples got ripe,
Beginning to fall.
Beginning to fall.
Beginning to fall.
The apples got ripe,
Beginning to fall.
Plop! Plop! Plop!

There came an old woman
A-picking them up.
Picking them up.
Picking them up.

There came an old woman
A-picking them up.
    Plop! Plop! Plop!

Old Ponto jumped up
And gave her a thump.
    Gave her a thump.
    Gave her a thump.
Old Ponto jumped up
And gave her a thump.
    Bump! Bump! Bump!

It made the old woman
Go hippity hop.
    Hippity hop!
    Hippity hop!
It made the old woman
Go hippity hop.
    Hop! Hop! Hop!

The bridle and saddle
Are up on the shelf.
    Up on the shelf!
    Up on the shelf!
The bridle and saddle
Are up on the shelf.
    Shelf! Shelf! Shelf!

If you want any more
You can sing it yourself.
    Self! Self! Self!

From *Did you Feed my Cow?* by Margaret Taylor (Thomas Y. Crowell, New York)

(See Note, page 153)

FOR THE STORYTELLER

For the Storyteller

IN MY first book, *A Storyteller's Choice*, I set out the essentials for successful storytelling, the principles all storytellers follow in the main, whether consciously or unconsciously. In this my second collection of stories, the same principles and methods apply and there seems no point, therefore, in trying to restate them in a different way. I have, however, replaced some of the examples with similar ones from this new selection of stories.

I would add one practical suggestion. It is a great help to keep a record of stories told, the sources from which they come and the type of audience that enjoyed them. If a working outline of a story is made, giving the names of the characters, the chief stages in the plot, the opening and closing sentences and repetitive phrases, it is a simple matter to revise the story quickly and to find a story for a special occasion.

Storytelling is an art, but one that, given the desire to succeed, may be acquired through practice and experience. Each one of us is a potential storyteller for we can all relate our own experiences with enthusiasm, conviction and a wealth of detail. This is because we are interested in what happens to ourselves, we have *seen* it happen and we want to tell others about it. Here are the essentials for successful storytelling: identification with what we tell, a clear picture of events and a desire to share the story with others.

Even in these days of the making and reading of many books, the story that is told by word of mouth holds its own. The spoken word is the memorable word and the voice and personality of the storyteller add richness to the story and lift it from the printed page into life.

All the stories in this book have given pleasure not only to countless listeners but also to me, for the first principle of choosing a story to tell is that it should appeal strongly to the storyteller. If it does not, he will tell it without conviction and the audience may well receive it with indifference. Every storyteller has to recognise that there are some stories that will never be his, although someone else may tell them with enthusiasm and success.

Whether stories should be learnt by heart, word for word, or told in one's own words, is a question I am often asked. This depends on both the storyteller and the story. It is easier for some people to learn a story by heart than to put it into their own words, others find it hampering to be con-fined to the actual words of the book. But the story itself must also be taken into consideration. There are some stories that have been told so perfectly by masters of their craft that there is no other way in which to tell them. So no one would use any but Rudyard Kipling's words for the *Just So Stories* and the stories of Hans Andersen, provided that a good translation is used, should be told as they are written. Traditional folk and fairy tales are in the perfect form for telling, for they have been handed down orally from genera-tion to generation.

When the time comes to choose a story, it is important to remember that not every story we read and like is suitable for telling, for what appeals to the eye and the mind may not appeal equally to the ear and the imagination. For effective telling the story must be direct and rich in action. Stories that are obviously unsuitable for telling as they stand should not be chosen by the inexperienced storyteller, but left until experience has given skill in adaptation.

Choose for your first stories to tell, therefore, those which are simple and dramatic and written in a suitable form for telling, as for example *Epaminondas* or *The Princess on the Glass Hill* in this book. There is a wealth of material in folk tale collections like those of Joseph Jacobs—*Mrs Vinegar, Tom Tit Tot*—or *Salt* (in this book) and *Baba Yaga* from

Arthur Ransome's *Old Peter's Russian Tales*. Wanda Gag's versions of Grimm's stories are just right for telling, as are also Andersen's simpler tales, *The Tinder-Box* or *The Swine-herd*. Once successful tellings have given confidence, the storyteller can experiment with different types of stories to find those that suit him best. For some it may be 'hero stories' such as Beowulf, King Arthur or Roland; for others fantasy by modern authors or realistic adventure as in *Jim Davis*, Masefield's smuggling story for boys. The scope for choice of stories is very wide and storytellers will find it useful to note down possible stories to tell as they come across them in their reading.

It is important that a storyteller should know a few stories really well as soon as possible. Librarians, teachers and others who tell stories are often asked for one at a moment's notice. If they can tell a story that is suitable for a mixed audience of adults and children, so much the better. Wanda Gag's *Gone is Gone*, Andersen's *The Nightingale*, Elizabeth Clark's *Brother Johannick and his Silver Bell*, are suitable for this purpose.

When the storyteller has had some experience, he will find that there are some stories he would like to tell that need adaptation in some way. The audience must be able to follow the story easily, for there can be no turning back to re-read as in a book. Descriptive passages have to be shortened, unnecessary complications of the plot deleted, some passages rephrased.

The way in which a story begins is of the utmost importance if it is to capture the child's interest and curiosity from the first moment. An old folk tale starts, 'A poor boy once hired himself out to a farmer for one marrow-fat pea a year', and at once the child is intrigued. But the first sentence in Andersen's *The Nightingale*, appears silly to children—of course the Emperor of China is a Chinaman!

Endings are equally important, for on these depend the impression left on the child's mind when the story is done.

He should be left with a relaxed feeling of satisfaction, for now the hero and the heroine are happy, the battles are over, the quest has been successful and right has triumphed. How pleasing to know for example, that Volkh is to become a Knight of the Golden Table, young as he is! Sometimes the feeling of finality can be achieved by the intonation of the voice only, at other times the last paragraph may have to be completely rephrased. Beware of the anti-climax when the interest of the story is really over. Whatever else is left to the inspiration of the moment, the first and last sentences of a story must always be memorised.

There can be no hard or fast rule for *learning* a story. For some memorising is no problem, for others it will be necessary to evolve some individual method of absorbing a story. What is *essential* is that the preparation is so thorough that when faced by an audience, there will be no uncertainty or fumbling for words.

A suggestion from long experience may be of help for the storyteller who finds it difficult to master a story. First read the story several times, carefully and with concentration. Then jot down an outline from memory, noting the stages in the development of the plot and the part the characters play. Read the story again to discover the places where it has not been clearly remembered. The secret of memorising a story, as Ruth Sawyer has said in her *The Way of the Storyteller*, and as all experienced storytellers know, is to *see* it as a series of pictures. The background, the people, the events must all be visualised before we can make others see them, too. In the same way, if we are really inside the story and can feel its mood, this will come to those who listen. *Live* with the story until it has been completely absorbed.

Now repeat the story *aloud*. Only in this way can we realise the tricks our memory can play us. A good vocabulary and an easy flow of words will help at this stage, but it is surprising how these improve with practice and growing confidence. The words we choose are as important as colours to a painter, for they are the means by which we interpret and give life to the stories we love.

When the day comes on which the story is to be told to an audience there should be no nervousness as long as it has been well chosen and prepared. We have something we want to share; the children wait expectantly, prepared to enjoy the story we have found for them. Remember to show them the book from which it comes, for a well told story often sends the child back to read more.

Tell the story in a natural and relaxed way, for story-telling is not a dramatic performance. There is a place for gesture and change of voice to indicate character, but only if these can be introduced naturally and spontaneously. The storyteller has only his voice, his personality, his faith in the story he has to tell. It is for the hearer to imagine the scene, to set the stage, to visualise the characters through the storyteller's interpretation.

Give any necessary explanations before the story begins, remembering that the child's imagination and the context often supply the answer. So, in the tale, *Where Arthur Sleeps*, there is no need to explain 'a sonorous clangour of bronze'. These are fine sounding words which give atmosphere and it matters not at all what they really mean.

Make full use of the 'dramatic pause' before important events or at a climax. Children have a quick mind and often guess what is going to happen, but a pause prolongs the suspense and gives the audience time to enjoy the pleasures of anticipation. Pace, too, is important, for timing is as vital in a story as in a play and can set the mood and strengthen the impact of what is happening. So the pace of the story of *Brother Johannick* will be slower than that of *Zini and the Witches*.

The voice is our instrument and it should be pleasant to hear and flexible in expressing shades of feeling or character. To be inaudible is unforgiveable and renders all our preparations useless. A few lessons on how to manage the voice without strain are invaluable. Technique can enable us to be heard anywhere, correct diction will ensure that we can be understood by anyone.

Whatever the story, if it is well chosen and carefully prepared it will give pleasure. As we tell it with warmth and enjoyment, we shall have our reward in the spontaneous response of the audience, whether it be laughter or emotion. 'In stories lie man's wisdom and knowledge and sense of beauty and wonder.'

EILEEN COLWELL

The Knockers

Telling time: 10–12 minutes.
Audience: Children of 7–10 upwards, especially boys.

Cornwall has always been rich in stories of fairies and giants and saints.* Until comparatively recently, professional storytellers called *Drolls* kept alive these ancient tales by word of mouth. The rocky shores with their caves and whirlpools and seals, the abandoned tin mines which still raise rusty machinery on the bleak headlands, the thickly wooded valleys, are a fit setting for folk-tales.

This story is based on the legends of the fairy people who live in the mines, no whimsy creatures these, but sturdy little men dressed as miners. Wheal Prudence, while not the name of a real place, might well be many places on the Cornish coast where the mineral-tinged streams flow down from the old workings and there are incredibly small tunnels bored by the miners of long ago.

The Knockers, written for reading aloud, lends itself to telling. It should be told in an easy conversational style and the dialect is suggested by the dialogue. Young boys delight in Billy's favourite exclamation, 'Blow me!', and indeed Billy Chenoweth, with his stiff black hair and blue eyes and his toughness and courage, is a boy's hero.

The Knockers' verse should be chanted in a suitable tone to indicate its supernatural origin. A word of explanation about Billy's journey down the shaft will help the children's imagination. Make it clear that the iron ladder is vertical and that it is very long indeed. Emphasise also that Billy is only nine years old, the age of some of the audience. Show the smallness of the Knockers, only two feet in height.

A good story which can be told just as it is written.

Salt

Telling time: 15–20 minutes.
Audience: Children of 8–10.

Ransome says in his introduction to *Old Peter's Russian Tales*, that he has 'taken his own way' with these old stories. The result is a collection that is ideal for the storyteller.

* See also: *Peter and the Piskies* by Ruth Manning-Sanders

The theme is familiar: the youngest son who, although a 'ninny', makes a fortune and marries the Princess. In Ransome's hands, the story develops unexpectedly and is graced with delightful touches of humour and even of tenderness. There is something innocent and childlike in the characters of Ivan himself, the little Princess and the old sailormen.

For help in memorising this story, note that it is in five stages and that these are told at a different pace. At the beginning when Ivan sets out on his strange voyage, he is still a ninny. With the discovery of the mountain of salt, he begins to take on character and vigour, and by the time he makes the deal with the Tzar, he is using his wits. Then comes the idyllic interlude of the little Princess's voyage with Ivan and lastly Ivan is thrown into the sea and makes his way back to the Princess. This last episode should be told briskly so that there is a sense of urgency, for the time is short in which to save the Princess.

If the story is too long, it is at the end that a cut could be made without detriment. Omit altogether the incident of the giant's visit to the wedding feast and conclude with Ransome's own final para-graph beginning, 'That is the story about salt. . . .'

As the story has been taken out of its context, I have omitted all reference to Old Peter and his grandchildren, as this breaks into the action.

Note the author's masterly use of prose in this smoothly flowing story with its Russian flavour, and his use of repetition—'the ancient old sailormen', 'a little ship, a little old ship.'

A delightful story with a theme of kindness and an attractive hero.

Epaminondas and his Auntie

Telling time: 6 minutes.
Audience: Children of 6 upwards.

No apology is needed for including this old favourite in a collection. It is a good story for inexperienced storytellers to begin with and it is useful in any storyteller's repertoire. Children gain added enjoyment from it because it is simple enough for them to anticipate what is going to happen.

Dialect is difficult and dangerous and if it cannot be done well, it should be left alone. An effect can be obtained by broadening the vowels so that Epaminondas drawls out his 'Ya-as, Mammy,' for instance. Epaminondas should not be shown as a half-wit; he is wide-eyed and innocent throughout and he does his best to obey his mother.

Mime adds greatly to the effectiveness of the story. Mime Epaminondas' actions and his Mammy's—for instance, really 'wrap it up in some leaves, put it in your hat and put your hat on your head. . . .' Make Epaminondas step right in the middle of each pie, but remember that there are only six. Don't hurry the story but pause significantly before Epaminondas does each wrong thing so as to give the audience time to anticipate what is about to happen.

There is one episode in the story which may distress little children, that is the death of the 'puppy-dog'. This seems unnecessary and it is quite enough to say that the dog is wet and miserable. Epaminondas can show by his tone that he is upset by what he has done and his mother can rub the puppy dry as she says, 'My gracious sakes alive, Epaminondas, you ain't got the sense you was born with!'

Omit the admonitory phrase which closes the story. It seems out of place to-day and in any case the story is over.

Brother Johannick and his Silver Bell

Telling time: 10–12 minutes.
Audience: Children of 9 upwards and adults.
Occasion: Christmas.

This is a simple but moving story. It does not need to be dramatic but should indicate the differing characters of the two chief persons in the story—Brother Johannick, old, gentle and saintly; Père Suliac, bluff and kind-hearted.

The story divides naturally into three parts. The first introduces Brother Johannick and gives the reason for his lonely sojourn on the little island. Then comes Christmas Eve with its contrasting scenes— the fog-encircled island with its bitter cold and the warmth and plenty of Père Suliac's home. The final episode builds up to the climax in which we see against a background of supernatural light, the weary old man and the radiant Child.

It has always seemed to me that the story should end with the woodcutter and Brother Johannick kneeling to give thanks to God for Christmas. All else is anti-climax. Personally I omit all references throughout the story to Père Suliac's clothing. For the children it is sufficient that he should wear a sheepskin coat. Any further details, although part of the original legend, distract attention from what matters in the story—Brother Johannick and his selfless service to mankind, and the gratitude and compassion shown to him by a simple man.

Children find the term *Gabariers* confusing and it has a harsh sound anyway. The familiar word 'Woodcutter' seems more suit-able here.

Volkh's Journey to the East

Telling time: 15–20 minutes.

Audience: Especially boys.

A reasonably easy story to tell but care must be taken to keep the wishes in the right order.

This story comes from a cycle of songs and ballads nearly a thousand years old. The Knights of the Golden Table were a brotherhood something like that of King Arthur and his Knights—both had a common aim, to bring about the triumph of Good over Evil.

There are several other stories that would be especially good for telling to boys in this collection, for example, *Vassily and Curly-Head the Brigand*. The story of Volkh is excellent, full of suspense and with an instant appeal because of the youth of the hero. I found when I told it for the first time, however, that it was too slow in beginning. What matters to the children is the tale of Volkh's six wishes and the rescue of little Prince Danilo. The secondary plot of the mother's emerald buckle which she has to give to the pilgrim, merely holds up the action and is of no importance to the story as a whole. Omit all mention of the buckle, therefore, but leave in Volkh's rescue of the pilgrim to explain the gifts he receives.

There is one other important point. Volkh has six wishes only, yet he uses *seven*—for a horse to carry him to Kiev, for a sword when the palace guard doubts his age, for his journey to find Danilo, to kill the hounds that threaten him, to open the cage, to provide a meal and to restore the prince's own clothes. This is the kind of mistake that children will notice, for the story is absorbing enough for them to count the wishes anxiously and to cry 'Silly idiot!' when Volkh thoughtlessly throws away his last wish. It is simple to omit the incident of the sword at the gates of the palace.

Make the most of the desperate situation when Volkh's wishes are gone and only one of Danilo's remains. Keep the audience in suspense—every child should be on the edge of his chair with anxiety in case the little Prince wastes his last wish.

The ending should come quickly and due solemnity should be given to the Prince's words as he makes Volkh a Knight of the Golden Table. This is an appealing story in which both the central characters are worthy of admiration.

Did you Feed my Cow?

Occasion: Just for fun and to work off some of the surplus energy of children.

The three chants for Caller and audience I have chosen are taken from an American collection of rhymes and games used by children in country lanes and city streets. Many are in modern slang and vernacular although their origin goes back a long way. These 'call and response' games have developed from a chant form peculiar to African music, as is seen in some Negro Spirituals.

I was introduced to these rhymes by Charlemae Rollins, a gifted American storyteller. It would be impossible for an English storyteller to give them the rhythm and verve—and the Southern States drawl—of this particular personality, but nevertheless, the rhymes can be great fun anywhere. There is no sense in them, just the pleasure of making a rhythmic noise and energetic movements. Not only do children enjoy them, but adults too.

The rhymes must be chanted rather than spoken and the Caller must set the rhythm, pace and mood with an infectious enthusiasm. The responses are simple and can be easily learned, the actions are those called for by the words and are expressive and spontaneous. Sobs must be properly mournful, thumps, bumps, flops, full of conviction and vigour. Forget your adult self-consciousness and let yourself go as the Caller. You will find the experience as exhilarating as the children do!

Bertha Goldfoot

Telling time: 10 minutes.
Audience: Children of 7 upwards, especially girls.

The stories in this collection are told by an old nurse while she is mending her charges' stockings. If the hole is small the story is short, if large the story is long. This was a medium-sized hole.

Perhaps the story is better told in the third person so that the storyteller—who is probably not in the least like an old nurse—does not get in the way. This will avoid the asides to her nurselings and will enable the storyteller to speed up the action occasionally. More detail can be assimilated in a story that is read than in one that is heard. For this reason the introductory part of the story might be shortened, although still retaining the author's own words, of course. It would then read thus:—

'Bertha's father was a baron. He had a castle on the banks of the Rhine and his castle nestled under the little village that paid him tribute. It was the custom for every villager to bring the Baron a gold piece a year; and even in the hard years he could not let them off because he himself had to pay tribute to the King. If he failed to do so the King might come down on him and seize his castle, and lands, and every-thing he had.

'When Bertha was born . . .'

It is important to emphasise the respective gifts of the Lorelei and the Stocking-Elf—even repeat them—for on this hangs the whole point of the story. When Bertha's right foot touches the ground for the first time, slow the pace of telling and use a dramatic pause, for this is the climax of the plot.

The humour of this story is of just the kind a child appreciates and it is an effective story for telling.

The Golden Phoenix

Telling time: 20 minutes.
Audience: Children of 8 upwards, especially boys.

A French-Canadian tale which has many variants in folk-lore. Michael Hornyansky's retelling is particularly effective for it has a spicy humour and mockery that keeps the audience laughing. There is good opportunity for characterisation here—the three brothers, their practical and authoritative father, the irascible Sultan and the charming Princess. Action and drama are plentiful and Petit Jean is an attractive hero. A story like this should be told at a good pace with vigour and a personal enjoyment of the fun. Allow time, how-ever, for the audience to savour the highlights of the hero's comic fight with the unicorn, the lion and the snake and his unusual game of hide-and-seek with the Sultan. This is a storyteller's version and needs no abridgment.

A librarian or teacher might well consider this as a possible story for dramatisation by a group of children. It would certainly be enjoyed by boys either as a mime play with a narrator or with speaking parts for the principal characters and any number desired of 'extras' as courtiers, soldiers and the like. Scenery need only be of the 'impressionist' kind and costumes from the dressing-up box. The animals could be represented by papier-mâché masks of a very simple kind. With such a story as a basis, the result could be fun for actors and audience.

The Hare, the Lions, the Monkey and Hare's Spotted Blanket

Telling time: 5 minutes.
Audience: Children of 7 upwards.

The stories of 'The Little Wise One' were collected by the author from natives in Central Africa who could neither read nor write nor speak in any other language than their own. Some of these stories are said to be centuries old. They are of the same origin as the 'Brer Rabbit' stories which came from Africa to the Southern States of America via the West Indies.

As usual the theme is of the triumph of the weaker and smaller animal over the stronger and larger by cunning. The fun of the story for children is Hare's 'colossal cheek' in tricking Lion, the King of the Beasts, into making a blanket for him and a spotted blanket at that! The story falls into two parts, Hare's ingenious way of getting Lion to make the blanket and the trick by which he makes Monkey the scapegoat and so secures the blanket for himself without fear of reprisals. Give the children time to wonder how Hare will get out of his predicament.

Hare's effrontery and conceit can be indicated by his supercilious tone in speaking to Lion's child and some gesture to suggest his strutting exit each time, for he is very conscious of his cleverness. Lion's child should be diffident and timid and in awe of this important stranger, Lion large and noisy. The short sentences and repetition help to make the point in this amusing story.

For similar stories see the *Anansi* stories from the West Indies, the *Brer Rabbit* stories and the collections made by Geraldine Elliot, for example, *The Long Grass Whispers.*

The Dancing Princesses

Telling time: 20 minutes.
Audience: Children of 7–10.
A story for the more experienced storyteller.

This story is De la Mare's version of Grimm's *The Dancing Shoes* and it will repay every storyteller to compare it with the original. The plot of the story remains the same, but how differently it is treated!

It has become an experience for both storyteller and children and has taken on enchantment and beauty.

It is a story for those who are happy with fantasy and enjoy the sound and rhythm of words. It will not be easy to learn but, once mastered, it will remain in the imagination and enrich it. Obviously it must be told in the author's own words as far as possible. The only place where it might be cut is in the meeting of the soldier with the old woman. To omit this seems a pity, for even the pig has individuality!

The story will begin quite smoothly and briskly for it has not yet taken on magic. From the moment when the soldier watches the beautiful princesses prepare for their midnight dancing, enchantment begins. 'In the filmy silver of the moon', 'to the music of harp and tambour and pipe', they dance until 'the scarlet shafts of morning' send them back to their beds. This dream-like atmosphere must shine through your story. Do not hurry over it but give the children time to savour the words and the pictures they evoke.

The ending is lighthearted for it is daylight again. The soldier is practical for he wants no royal marriage but asks only to sit on the throne for a moment and to have as a gift—some pigs! He has pity for the princesses too, like the kindly man he is, and asks that they may be forgiven and marry the princes of their choice. How different from Grimm's ending with its punishments!

And so to the last sentences which should be spoken quietly for the soldier, down-to-earth as he is, has his dreams too, as do we all.

A story which will be a source of pleasure to children and will reward those who store it in their memory.

The Goat Well

Telling time: 10 minutes.
Audience: Children of 10–11.

The collection from which this story comes is an American one made by the well-known student of folklore, Harold Courlander. The tales were collected from the people of the country, ranging from an elderly priest to a young boy, for storytelling is still an essential part of life in Ethiopia.

The theme is a common one, the too-credulous man tricked by the quicker-witted rogue. It is told, as are all stories which are handed down orally, with economy and effect. The humour is pithy, the characterisation definite, the story down-to-earth. It will be appreciated by the child who prefers realism to fantasy.

Make the rogue, Woharia, plausible and smooth, the Cunama excitable, for he is in great anxiety lest he lose the well, he implores the goats to materialise, he is in a frenzy when he thinks the villagers are mocking him. Increase the pace, therefore, for the Cunama. The two characters afford a good contrast.

There is no need to shorten the story except that it seems un-necessary to describe the Cunama's reception at the villages three times over. The story ends quickly—as it should—but the final sentence needs to be a little stronger. It might read like this perhaps :—

'And this time the trader was so happy that he *did* dance in the market-place, while the people clapped their hands and the drummer beat upon his drum. Justice had been done!'

The Snooks Family

Telling time: 5 minutes.

Audience: Children under 10, especially boys.

Occasion: At the end of a storytelling session or at a children's party.

Harcourt Williams included this story in his collection, *Tales from Ebony*, 'just for fun'. He told me that he had no idea of its origin, but remembered that his father often told it to him when they were out walking and the way seemed long.

This is an audience-participation story for children still young enough not to be self-conscious. Let the children themselves try blowing in all these odd ways. It will be an hilarious performance, all the more so for being a rather spluttery one! The story is so simple, yet so absurd, that it is easily remembered and children love to try it out on their friends and relations.

Jean Labadie's Big Black Dog

Telling time: 12–15 minutes.

Audience: Children of 10 upwards.

The stories in this collection were told to the author's mother by her great-uncle, a *coureur de bois* in French Canada. They were acted so dramatically that everyone who listened could *see* what was happen-ing. A story of this kind needs to be told in the same way to-day, with gesture, excitement and drama.

It must be made quite clear from the beginning that Jean's dog is imaginary or the story will fall flat. Once the children have grasped this, they can appreciate the building up of the character of the big black dog and the way in which more and more people *think* that they have really seen it.

Every time anyone in the story describes the dog, they must do so very dramatically with wide, descriptive gestures—'with his big red tongue hanging out . . . lifting one paw this way and another paw that way.' In fact mime is useful throughout the story.

Jean soon finds that his invention has got out of hand, in fact at times he almost believes in his dog himself. There is a dramatic surprise when Jean having taken his dog back to the Indians is greeted on his return by André—'It's about your big black dog . . .', says André, and the storyteller should pause here so that everyone wonders what is coming. The climax is in doubt until the last possible moment when Jean shoots his dog. Not only is it a shock to the people in the story but to us as well!

A clever and witty story, with much wisdom behind it, that has stood the test of time for its humour and drama.

The Princess on the Glass Hill

Telling time: 10 minutes.

Audience: Boys and girls of 7–10.

An easy story to tell.

This traditional story appears in *East o' the Sun and West o' the Moon,* but I think I read it originally in Sir George W. Dasent's collection, now out of print. My own version is the result of audience-reaction over the years and I realise that details have been altered or omitted during the process. The storyteller who uses my book will probably in his turn tell the story in his own words, for this is the way folk tales are kept alive. All that matters is that the telling should be spontaneous.

Make the most of the dramatic details—the clash of thunder and the earthquakes, the horses which appear, the mysterious knight in his flashing armour. Here is material for a lively story in which the storyteller can let himself go!

The story is in two parts, each set against a different backcloth. The first is night-time in a lonely barn in the meadow; the second the shining Glass Hill and the Princess, with the gorgeous array of princes to give added colour. Add your own descriptive touches as you see the pictures in your imagination.

Note the use of repetitive phrases. This is deliberate, for it is part of the pattern of folk-tales.

The ending is doubly satisfactory, for the Princess is marrying our old friend, Boots, and Boots is scoring over his disagreeable elder brothers. Younger members of a family will appreciate this victory particularly!

Zini and the Witches

Telling time: 20 minutes.

Audience: Boys and girls of 8–10.

Occasion: Hallowe'en.

Stories for Hallowe'en are not easy to find, but here is an unusual one that should please, especially if told with relish on the part of the storyteller and in the suitably flickering light of a turnip lantern.* Children delight in 'witchy' stories, so make the most of the Black Magic and the eerie meeting at which the Chief Witch sits on a bat amidst the covey of witches in the guise of vultures, lynxes, owls and cats. The story is told with such a sense of humour—the Witch-wife turns into a *pink* cat—that there is no fear of nightmares. In any case most children are not nearly as sensitive in this respect as many adults fear. The witch's incantation over her husband should be chanted as fiendishly as possible, so that the children realise that this seemingly harmless lullaby has a double meaning.

The story falls into three parts—Zini's battle against his wife's spells, his long ordeal under enchantment, his final release and the defeat of his wicked wife. The pace should slow down in the middle of the story to convey the eternity during which Zini suffers from cold and heat, hunger and thirst as he lies motionless on the horribly narrow ledge. With the coming of the Squirrels, the story gathers pace and cheerfulness.

Note the delightful touches as, for instance, the Baby Squirrel's dance on Zini's moccasin—how like a human child's 'Just look at me!' The characters are very real and Zini has our sympathy from the beginning in his fear of the unknown. The Witch-wife—as children have remarked with pleasure—is a 'proper Witch'.

There is nothing superfluous here. Every part of the story is necessary and can be appreciated by children.

Note that the theme of the story is Good versus Evil and that although Good is under an eclipse for a time, it triumphs in the end. An effective and amusing story which the storyteller can tell with drama—and not too seriously.

*Note that an effective lantern is much more easily made from a melon than from a turnip!

Where Arthur Sleeps

Telling time: 10–12 minutes.
Audience: Children of 8 upwards, especially boys.

Stories of King Arthur are always in demand. The legend that Arthur and his host still sleep until the day of great danger is one that is known in many places. This version is told by a Welshman who has used his Celtic imagination to good effect. His phrasing has a Welsh lilt which comes over even if the storyteller cannot reproduce the intonation of Welsh speech.

The word picture of the scene in the cave is most vivid. See it in your own imagination, feel the silence which has been unbroken for centuries—surely the interlopers would speak in whispers. Then comes the clangour of the bell and the three dread voices, one as 'light as a bird's', another 'as dark as a bull's', the third coldly menacing. If you cannot see this scene and feel its drama, you have no vocation as a storyteller.

Make the Welshman edge round the bell very slowly while the children hold their breath. Will he manage it, especially the third time? Then suddenly increase the pace as the bell clangs, the warriors spring to their feet, the war horses neigh. Into this tumult, so terrifying because of its former silence, drops Arthur's calm and authoritative voice.

The ending is more effective if the story finishes after the thief is thrown out and the storyteller goes straight on to the prophecy, repeating it slowly and impressively.

Children love words so don't deprive them of 'a sonorous clangour of bronze', or 'the hooves of the horses effulgent as autumn's moon'. Roll such phrases round your tongue and give them their full value.

A dramatic story told with humour, vigour and enjoyment by the author—and the storyteller, too.